Uncommon Sense

Uncommon Sense

*The Life and Thought
of Ludwig von Bertalanffy
(1901-1972),
Father of General Systems Theory*

Mark Davidson

Foreword by R. Buckminster Fuller
Introduction by Kenneth E. Boulding

J.P. TARCHER, INC.
Los Angeles
Distributed by Houghton Mifflin Company
Boston

Library of Congress Cataloging in Publication Data

Davidson, Mark.
    Uncommon Sense.

    Bibliography: p.227
    Includes index.
    1. Bertalanffy, Ludwig von, 1901-1972.
2. Scientists—Canada—Biography. 3. System theory.
I. Title.
Q143.B45D38 1983   003'.092'4 [B] 82-16900
ISBN 0-87477-165-x

J.P. TARCHER, INC.
9110 Sunset Blvd.
Los Angeles, CA 90069

Design by Thom Dower

Manufactured in the United States of America

S 10 9 8 7 6 5 4 3 2 1

First Edition

To the memory of Maria von Bertalanffy (1904–1981), whose final act of devotion to her husband was to assist me with the research for this book.

To my wife, Nirmali, for her loving and intellectual support.

To publisher Jeremy Tarcher, for his guidance and patience, but mostly for his enthusiasm.

And to senior editor Janice Gallagher, for suggesting that I write the book and then steering it through its three-year voyage to completion.

Contents

PREFACE

A book about Ludwig von Bertalanffy's thought is long overdue.

Arthur Koestler (in a letter to this author)

He inspired me. He stimulated me. I am glad that somebody is going to present Ludwig von Bertalanffy to the world.

Karl Menninger (in a letter to this author)

. . . one of those strategically placed thinkers whose knowledge in many fields permits them . . . to penetrate to the quick of the living reality.

Aldous Huxley (in a letter to Bertalanffy)

Ludwig von Bertalanffy may well be the least known intellectual titan of the twentieth century. As the father of the interdisciplinary school of thought known as general systems theory, he made important contributions to biology, medicine, psychiatry, psychology, sociology, history, education, and philosophy. Yet he spent his life in semi-obscurity, and he survives today mostly in footnotes.

I first learned of Bertalanffy's existence in December 1979—more than seven years after his death—from my editor, Janice Gallagher. Knowing of my love for science writing, she suggested that I might like the challenge of assembling his insights in a conceptual biography.

My first few weeks of research, during which I discovered that Bertalanffy's scientific contribution had been literally encyclopedic, left me thoroughly intimidated. I feared that I might never finish.

But I decided to make the commitment when I discovered that Bertalanffy had espoused a single standard of morality, which is a viewpoint I find irresistibly appealing because it is extremely rare and (to my mind) absolutely necessary if humanity is to survive. For Bertalanffy, a wrongful act was equally wrong whether perpetrated by capitalist or communist, archbishop or atheist, professor or pipe-fitter, friend or foe.

Perhaps one reason so few people advocate a single standard of morality is that it can make the advocate's life quite unrewarding. Those who point out that all emperors are naked are not likely to be invited to join anybody's royal court. Citizens of the world are in constant jeopardy of becoming persons without a country.

As a citizen of the world, Bertalanffy opposed Hitlerism, Stalinism, McCarthyism, jingoism on both sides of the Cold War, and chauvinism in the Third World. As a single-standard-bearer in general, he was a scientist who repudiated the arrogance of scientism, a biologist who rejected the heredity-is-everything dogma of biologism, a laboratory researcher who questioned the absolute value of empiricism, an agnostic who denounced materialism, an advocate of social planning who championed individualism, and a systems science pioneer who warned that systems science could be used for totalitarianism.

With that much intellectual independence, the wonder is not that Bertalanffy was rather obscure but that he was permitted to leave any mark on the world at all.

At any rate, he further contributed to his obscurity by

failing to organize his literary output. As he wryly acknowledged, his body of thought was "dispersed in many places and therefore not easy to see as an organized system."

He did produce three organized books on theoretical biology. But the bulk of his multidisciplinary contributions were dispersed in more than two hundred articles in scientific journals and other scholarly periodicals. His general-interest books were either edited lectures or smorgasbords of lectures and papers on his systems thought. In the main, Bertalanffy's literary estate can be compared to a massive assortment of jigsaw-puzzle pieces, with numerous duplicates and gaps. Missing from this mélange is any single picture that integrates his biological, psychological, social, and philosophical thought.

I was extremely fortunate, therefore, that my effort received the cooperation of many eminent scientists and scholars (quoted throughout my text) and also the two persons closest to Bertalanffy. In the latter case, I refer to Bertalanffy's son, Felix D. Bertalanffy, a professor of anatomy and a cancer researcher at the University of Manitoba in Winnipeg, and Bertalanffy's wife, Maria, who offered me the hospitality of the suburban home she and her husband had shared during his last position, as a professor at the State University of New York in Buffalo. Maria, who died of a heart attack October 6, 1981, had been the companion and editorial assistant of Ludwig von Bertalanffy for nearly half a century. She helped me attempt the mind-boggling task of synthesizing her husband's intellectual estate by opening up to me his files, including tape recordings of university classes and seminars that Bertalanffy had conducted during the last two years of his life. Maria also unlocked the treasure of her marital memories, beginning with the day in 1924 when, as she recalled, "I fell in love with Ludwig's brain."

Bertalanffy's legacy is an imposing monument of contemporary thought, not just because of its extraordinary diversity, but also for its insight into an organizing force that links us all to a cosmic unity. It is the universal force that arranges the elements of reality into the entities called systems. It is a force, Bertalanffy warned, that we must no longer take for granted if we are to solve the uniquely complex and perilous problems of today's world.

Philosopher John Stuart Mill, writing in the middle of the nineteenth century, observed that "no great improvements in the lot of man are possible until a great change takes place in the fundamental constitution of our modes of thought." In our own time, Albert Einstein declared that "we shall require a substantially new manner of thinking if mankind is to survive." I believe that new manner of thinking was developed by Ludwig von Bertalanffy.

This book, then, is for anyone who is weary of hearing warnings that humanity is courting extinction, and who would prefer to consider alternatives.

It is for anyone looking for a pattern behind the seeming chaos of our personal and public lives, anyone trying to understand why many if not most of our attempts to solve complex problems are failing.

It is for anyone facing the awesome responsibility of making decisions that affect other people—anyone including parents, pedagogues, and public officials.

It is for systems engineers, analysts, and managers who would like to explore the systems approach at its ultimate frontiers.

It is for specialists and students in any discipline who would like to see how their role relates to the human condition.

And it is for those who—in the words of a poem by Heinrich Heine—have ever wondered, "What meaning has man? From where has he come? Where does he go?"

PASADENA, JANUARY 1983   MARK DAVIDSON

FOREWORD

In 1972 I was asked by a committee of French scientists to write a paper on Ludwig von Bertalanffy's nomination for the Nobel Prize. I did so. The nomination went to Oslo, but the committee's effort came just too late. Ludwig died before their nomination of him could be considered by the Nobel authorities.

Though more than a decade has passed, I have had to alter only the first paragraph of that paper to adapt it as a foreword to this excellent book.

To appreciate the enormous contribution to science and humanity of Dr. Ludwig von Bertalanffy, it is necessary to comprehend the state of knowledge and on-going research of his time.

Among the many unprecedented human gains of the twentieth century, none have been greater than those in education and in the increasing numbers of students continuing through postgraduate scholarship. This educational explosion has been accompanied by an ever more sharply focused specialization. Humanity seems to have been convinced that specialization is natural, logical and desirable. But specialization precludes the advantage of synergy, which is the behavior of whole systems unpredicted by the separate behavior of any of the system's parts. Synergy is physically manifested by the mass interattractions cohering the physical universe. For instance, no characteristic of the moon *per se* predicts that it will be attracted by the Earth and vice versa, nor that both will attract and be attracted by other planets and by the sun. It is also a corollary of synergy that the known behavior of two or more of its parts often leads to discovery not only of data regarding other parts of the system but also to discovery of the coexistence of as yet unknown parts of that whole. For instance, the application of Newton's mass attraction law to the behaviors of the solar system's known planetary parts indicated the required presence of two as yet undiscovered planets and indicated as well their probable sizes and positions at specific times.

So too did the Greeks' known 180-degree sum of the angles of a triangle and the known behavior of two of the triangle's six parts make possible the synergetic discovery of the relative magnitude of the four unknown parts.

It is notable that these synergetically advantaged scientific strategies, in the pursuit of scientific knowledge, were formulated long before the educational explosion and its narrowing professional preoccupations.

The era of specialization has witnessed the general disappearance of natural philosophers like Whitehead. Comprehensive thinking has dwindled and almost vanished.

A consequence of the epochal abandonment of broad consideration by scientists and scholars of the applied significance to humanity of their specialized preoccupations has been a forfeiture of all the gains of synergy to politically underwritten corporate exploitations of the ever-multiplying inventory of technological gains.

After Hiroshima and its wholesale killing of innocents, the public began to protest what mistakenly seemed to be the exclusively negative effects of science. The public began holding scientists responsible for the political abuses of its discoveries. Circa 1950 the *Bulletin of Atomic Scientists* was published in a sense of general guilt and in the hope that its member-readers might be able to persuade public policymakers to divert application of their findings from lethal to vital uses. The public and the scientists together assumed that the scientists held an exercisable initiative in public policy-making. But despite the protests, the socio-economic crises increase rather than diminish. As a consequence of the twentieth-century abandonment of synergetical thinking, both scholars and the public in general have been so disintegrated by ultraspecialization as to be not only helpless to alter public policy but also uninformed regarding comprehensive evolutionary trends underlying the forces at work around the planet.

Unique amongst the sciences, biochemistry and biophysics have long been aware of the synergetic character of ecological macro-systems and of micro-synergetical phenomena in general. As a perpetuator of natural philosophy from previous centuries and as a scientific pioneer of the present century, Ludwig von Bertalanffy was the first to undertake a mathematically rigorous approach to the understanding of biochemical synergies. He thus came to both evolve and name general systems theory, which concept and schematic strategies first seek out the parameters or known behaviors of the hypothetically considered whole— hypothetical because what constitutes the whole of biological life has as yet defied the clear-cut finiteness characterizing the Greek's triangle. That Ludwig von Bertalanffy and other physiological pioneers have as yet to be rewarded with the finite system clarity attained by Euclid, Newton, and others, in no way diminishes the brilliance of von Bertalanffy's conceptualizing nor the contribution that his general systems theory has made to vast fields of scientific inquiry and the scientific organization of human efforts in general.

R. BUCKMINSTER FULLER

INTRODUCTION

W riters, thinkers, and scientists can no doubt be divided into those who are behind their time, those
who are with their time, and those who are before their
time. The first disappear into obscurity, the second become
famous and fill the history books, and the third have to
wait to be recognized. Newton, Darwin and others belong
to the second class. Roger Bacon, Mendel, and the early
proponents of continental drift are examples of the third.

Ludwig von Bertalanffy certainly falls into the third category. In his lifetime he received very little recognition, except in a small circle of admirers, which included myself.
He is recognized indeed as the founding father of general
systems. The Society for General Systems Research has an
annual Bertalanffy Lecture, but this is a very small group,
and so far has not really penetrated very far into the universities, still less the school systems. There are virtually no
departments for general systems; and where it is taught,
it is usually as a sideline rather than as a prime responsibility
of some discipline or department.

Nevertheless, I strongly suspect that von Bertalanffy will
be much more prominent in the histories of scientific

thought yet to be written than he appears now. We are in the middle of a quiet revolution in virtually all the sciences, which is largely the development of what might be called "post-Newtonian science." It involves the recognition that equilibrium systems are extremely rare, in fact strictly nonexistent, though temporary quasi-equilibrium systems are found in such things as celestial mechanics and climactic ecosystems. The universe has been a big disequilibrium process from its inception. The new trend in science also recognizes the importance of rare, improbable, even unique events. We see this in the strangeness of twentieth-century physics; in the development of chemistry "far from equilibrium" by Prigogine; in the rise of plate tectonics in geology and paleontology; in the development of a "punctuational" rather than "gradualist" evolutionary theory, going a long way beyond Darwin; in the increasing dissatisfaction with equilibrium theory in economics and sociology, and so on. Bertalanffy's work, both in the theory of the development of the organism and in his general evolutionary theory, anticipated this movement in many ways, no doubt imperfectly but at the same time profoundly.

Bertalanffy came into my own life like a comet. I became aware of his work at a distance, as it were, in the 1950s when I was conducting a seminar in the integration of the social sciences at the University of Michigan in Ann Arbor. Almost without my knowing it, it turned into a seminar in general systems, even before I had heard the phrase. Then Bertalanffy and I, together with Anatol Rapoport and Ralph Gerard, the four founding fathers of the Society for General Systems Research, turned up in Stanford at the Center for Advanced Study in the Behavioral Sciences, the newly established Ford Foundation enterprise, in the fall of 1954. The story has often been told of how we sat around the lunch table one day, not long after we gathered, and it became clear that we were all converging on something like general systems from different directions, Bertalanffy's thought certainly seeming to be the most advanced. Somebody said, "Let's form a society." So we called a meeting at the American Association for the Advancement of Science meeting in December of that year in Berkeley. Some seventy people came and there was a lot of enthusiasm; the Society got off the ground, originally as the Society for the Advancement of General Systems Theory. Then, the following fall, Anatol Rapoport and Ralph Gerard joined me at the University of Michigan, and the Society got underway. In the meantime Bertalanffy began his peregrination through a variety of rather remote institutions, and I did not meet him again more than two or three times.

I now find it hard to identify how much of my subsequent work and writing was influenced by the nine months that we spent together in Stanford. I am sure it must have been a great deal. At the meeting of the American Economic Association in Denver in 1980, a young man came up to me and looked me in the eye and said, "My professors warned me about you. You sold your soul to the biologists." If I did, Bertalanffy was certainly one of the brokers, and it was a very good investment. Mr. Davidson is to be congratulated for recreating in this volume, for the world to read, the image of a man I remember as being like no other—kindly, rather shy, a curious mixture of confidence that he was saying something important and diffidence that grew out of the lack of people to receive it. He presented a facade that was almost a caricature of the Viennese professor, but behind the facade one felt a remarkable mind and spirit with an extraordinary sense both of the immense complexity of the real world and strong faith that it was not wholly beyond our grasp.

KENNETH E. BOULDING*

*Boulding, whose many books include *The Organizational Revolution* and *The Meaning of the Twentieth Century*, is a former president of the Society for General Systems Research, the American Economic Association, and the American Association for the Advancement of Science.

1

General Systems Theory:
A PRESCRIPTION FOR SURVIVAL

I heartily agree that the main objection against current philosophy is its . . . reliance on so-called common sense. . . . Society [has] become so complex that traditional ways and means are not sufficient anymore. Approaches of a holistic or systems nature have to be introduced.

Ludwig von Bertalanffy, in his
foreword to Ervin Laszlo's
Introduction to Systems Philosophy

Common sense, which once assured humanity that the world is flat, now assures us that the world is the sum of its parts.

As a result, most of us deal with our environment by taking it apart—piece by piece, problem by problem—on the assumption that our efforts ultimately will add up to success.

The human race has gotten by with that piecemeal approach for centuries, just as it managed to get by for centuries with the pre-Copernican notion of a flat earth. But our age of innocence must now end. The unprecedented interconnectedness of civilization compels us to face the fact that the world is greater than the sum of its parts. We therefore must begin paying attention to the fate of the whole earth rather than just the sum of its nations.

Similarly, contemporary crises compel us to consider the

whole society rather than just its separate groups, and the whole person rather than just the person's separate roles.

On nearly every level of our life, challenges have become too complex to yield to orthodox analytic approaches that deal with interrelated problems in artificial isolation. Nationally, we are faced by an interactive linkage of government budgets, interest rates, housing, employment, poverty, welfare, taxes, and crime. Internationally, we are confronted by an interactive linkage of population, food, natural resources, industry, technology, commerce, and conflict. And the overlap between international and national spheres is constantly enlarging.

Everywhere, we are involved with immensely complex systems that authorities call counter-intuitive, because these systems do not necessarily behave as common sense leads us to expect. And everywhere, we are faced with a set of problems that authorities call a *problematique:* a veritable Rubik's Cube in which the solution of one facet by itself can actually be a step backward from overall progress.

We have abruptly entered a new history, an era that demands a science and philosophy of synthesis.

We need—all of us need—a new way of thinking.

We need a way of clearly seeing the forest for the trees, a new perspective that is variously described as holistic, ecological, gestalt, global, molar, integrative, organismic, synergistic, synergetical, synholistic, and systems.

We need, in short, an uncommon sense of interactive relationships within and between wholes. Not just the occasional holistic insight that some of us experience in one realm or another as we muddle through life, but a total vision of the holistic landscape.

Though this fundamental shift in outlook has been advocated by numerous twentieth-century thinkers—including English mathematician-philosopher Alfred North Whitehead, South African statesman-philosopher Jan Christiaan Smuts, and American architect-inventor-philosopher R. Buckminster Fuller—only one gave the cause a solid foundation of both science and humanism: biologist-philosopher Ludwig von Bertalanffy (1901–1972).

A professor of biology and a biological researcher in Austria, England, Canada, and the United States, Bertalanffy achieved international recognition for his discoveries in the comparative physiology of metabolism and growth, for the Bertalanffy Growth Equations used around the world to predict the yield in fisheries, and for the Bertalanffy Method for early detection of cancer.

But his principal interests were conceptual. At the age of twenty-five, he wrote *Modern Theories of Development*, in which he focused on embryonic development in a classic presentation of the organismic-systems viewpoint in biology. With massive evidence and rigorous logic, he advanced "the necessity of regarding the living organism as an organized system," and he defined "the fundamental task of biology as the discovery of the laws of biological systems," by which he meant the laws under which an organism's parts and processes are organized for the survival of the whole.

A man of vast erudition and curiosity, he soon began to wonder if laws of biological systems—governing such processes as growth and adaptation—might apply to areas beyond biology. He reasoned: if the law of gravity applies equally to apples and planets, and if the law of probability applies equally to genetics and life insurance, then laws of biological systems might well be applicable to the human psyche, to social institutions, and to the whole global ecosphere. And that would mean Bertalanffy's conceptual model of the living organism as an *open system*, an entity continuously interacting with its environment, contained revolutionary implications for behavioral and social science.

By the age of thirty-six, Bertalanffy developed the hypothesis that there are natural laws of organization governing systems on *all* levels of existence, and he began advocating an interdisciplinary search for such laws. To that end, he shared ideas with scientists and scholars in many fields, as a fellow of the Rockefeller Foundation, a founding fellow of the Center for Advanced Study in the Behavioral Sciences, a visiting professor at the Menninger Foundation, a consultant to the mental health section of the World Health

Organization, an honorary fellow of the American Psychiatric Association, a founder of the International Center for Integrative Studies, and a founder of the Society for General Systems Research.

Bertalanffy thus became known as the father of *general systems theory* (*GST*). The term has confused many English-speaking readers, because it is a mistranslation of Bertalanffy's original, German-language proposal for *Allgemeine Systemlehre*, by which he meant a general systems *teaching*.

As Bertalanffy confessed to his wife, Maria, he wished he had given his proposal another name in English. Maria explained to me: "People kept asking Ludwig to tell them what the general systems theory is. When he began his answer by explaining that there is no actual theory, they became disappointed and wouldn't pay enough attention to the rest of what he had to say."

The rest of the answer is the subject of this book. Bertalanffy's general systems theory, in one sense, was a proposed scientific discipline that would strive for a unity of science by seeking principles common to systems in general. It was a dream of perhaps the ultimate scientific breakthrough, in which basic knowledge about all systems might provide humanity with unprecedented powers of prediction and control—in physical, biological, behavioral and sociological realms.

Though Bertalanffy's proposed discipline for all disciplines attracted the interest of scientists in many fields and nations, it is still only a hope on the intellectual horizon. But Bertalanffy, like Columbus, succeeded brilliantly while falling short of his goal. To quote one of his favorite phrases, he devoted himself to "exploring a continent previously missed," a vast frontier of systems perspective. His observations as a systems explorer appear likely to be of value to humanity for centuries to come, regardless of when or whether Bertalanffy's general systems orientation is established as a formal discipline.

Because of Bertalanffy's extensive contributions to systems thought, his term *general systems theory* became synonymous in some scientific literature with his wide-ranging *general systems approach:* a way of looking at problems with insights gleaned from knowledge about systems in general. Gradually, Bertalanffy's general systems theory acquired that meaning—of an approach, attitude, viewpoint, or worldview—in much of his own writing. *And that expanded meaning of GST will be used in this book, except when otherwise indicated.*

Bertalanffy's general systems approach, to make this clear right from the start, is much broader than the systems approaches usually associated with engineering, corporate management, and public administration. Bertalanffian GST applies the principles of integrated thinking to all areas of human experience. Therefore, as I hope to demonstrate in this book, there's a world of difference between the technical systems approaches and the all-encompassing GST mode of thinking that Bertalanffy had in mind. So don't be mislead by the fact that the two domains overlap.

Now, I don't mean to give the impression that Bertalanffy presented his GST as a panacea. He repeatedly disassociated himself from the ranks of systems hucksters, such as the freelance "general systems consultant" who recently sent me a self-promoting booklet describing GST as "a fairly easy way to deal with the world around us in all its complexities." Neither Bertalanffy nor any other contributor to general systems thought ever said that the general systems approach is easy. He never suggested that GST would show anyone how to lose weight, win friends, or build a better mousetrap. He did believe, however, that GST would help us think more clearly about whatever our goals happen to be, and about what methods we should use to achieve them. And he believed the first step was to become aware of the concept *system.*

The Nature of Systems

A system, in Bertalanffy's terminology, is any entity maintained by the mutual interaction of its parts, from atom to cosmos, and including such mundane examples as telephone, postal, and rapid transit systems. A Bertalanffian system can be physical like a television set, biological like a cocker spaniel, psychological like a personality, sociological like a labor union, or symbolic like a set of laws. A system can also be a categorical combination, like the man-machine system that composes a factory. A system can be static like a crystal, mechanical like a clock, mechanically self-regulating like a thermostat, and organismically interactive with the environment, like plants, people, and populations.

A system can be composed of smaller systems and can also be part of a larger system, just as a state or province is composed of smaller jurisdictions and also is part of a nation. Consequently, the same organized entity can be regarded as either a system or a subsystem, depending on the observer's focus of interest. The hierarchical nature of systems is itself a basic pattern or organization, as in such ascending levels of organized complexity as atom, molecule, cell, organ, organism, group, society, world, solar system, galaxy, universe.

The common denominator of the various definitions of *system* is the idea of interaction. On various occasions, Bertalanffy defined a system as "a set of elements standing in interaction," "a complex of components in mutual interaction," "a complex of interacting elements," and "a dynamic order of parts and processes standing in mutual interaction." A co-founder of the general systems movement, biomathematician Anatol Rapoport (1911–), defines a system as "a whole that functions as a whole by virtue of the interaction of its parts," adding that "a system, roughly speaking, is a bundle of relations." Hence, a watch functions as a system, but it becomes just a heap of parts if it is disassembled. Likewise, when *Star Wars* robot C3P0 was disassembled in an act of villainy, he lost all semblance of personality and became just a collection of mute junk. A watch and a robot, as systems, are entities that emerge from the organized relationship of their parts.

A system is a manifestation of something intangible, but quite real, called organization. A system, like a work of art, is a pattern rather than a pile. Like a piece of music, it's an arrangement rather than an aggregate. Like a marriage, it's a relationship rather than an encounter.

Organization means nothing to an aggregate, like a bunch of peanuts, and it means everything to a system, like a peanut farm. To a system, organization is a matter of life and death. A dog may be man's best friend, but an assortment of his chemical components will never fetch your morning newspaper.

You are more than your constituent ingredients of a few gallons of water and assorted quantities of fat, carbon, lead, phosphorus, iron, lime, magnesium, and sulfur. You are the organization of your parts. Disrupt your organization, and you die. Conversely, though the cell population of your body repeatedly dies and is replaced, you survive because your organization survives. You exist as an expression of a universal force of organization, a force that coordinates about 10 billion cells in your brain and approximately 100 trillion cells in your body. It is a force, like gravity, that is too mysterious to explain—nobody knows what gravity *is*—but too common to ignore.

There is nothing mysterious, in the perspective of science, about the idea that a system is greater than the sum of its parts. No ghost need be summoned for an explanation: a system is greater than the sum of its parts because a system consists of the parts plus the way the parts relate to each other and the qualities that emerge from those relationships.

Some of our Stone Age ancestors employed the concept of system for their survival. At first, they lived on the perpetual edge of extinction, relying on hand-held stones that they shaped and sharpened to serve as tools for defense and hunting. Then they became masters of their environment as a result of being inspired to make tools of two or more different parts. They used stray vines to tie their sharpened stones to a wooden handle, thereby producing the first axes. Similarly, they produced the first spears by attaching a pointed flint-stone to a wooden rod. Gradually, they invented an entire arsenal of such composite tools, each providing more total power than its components could have provided independently. That systems breakthrough marked the beginning of technology and the prelude to civilization.

In a system, one and one equals two *plus*. The *plus* is the relationship signified by the connective word *and*, as in Laurel and Hardy, Gilbert and Sullivan, or Bonnie and Clyde. In systems thinking, the *fundamental* reality is the relationship of parts, not the substance. The crucial aspect is form. Rodin's *The Thinker* is equally pensive in marble, brass or clay. No matter how many times you change the cast of *Hamlet*, it's pretty much the same *Hamlet*, because the play's the thing. No matter how many times despots are deposed, the despotism remains pretty much the same if there is no change in the form of the social system. Generally, the personality of a leader is less decisive than the personality of the organization.

The components of a system display their full range of traits only by interacting—among themselves and with their environment—like bees in a beehive, flocks of birds, schools of fish, herds of animals, and groups of people. For better or worse, teams and mobs perform in ways of which individual members may be incapable.

Systems thinking is vital to a real understanding of a relationship like marriage, where "us" is significantly more than the simple addition of "you" and "me," and where the birth of a child adds considerably more than a third of new complexity, contrary to the old song that says "and Baby makes three."

Systems of human relationships tend to be more complex than they seem because of qualities that emerge from the relationships themselves. In accordance with this *principle of emergence*, systems have characteristics that emerge from the interaction of their parts, the way wetness emerges from the interaction of two parts of hydrogen and one part of oxygen. The same holistic magic occurs when a composer arranges notes to form a musical composition, when an artist arranges dabs of pigment to form a painting, and when a writer assembles lifeless words to form a work of living literature. The Nobel laureate poet of India, Rabindranath Tagore (1861–1941), expressed the principle of emergence when he wrote: "By plucking her petals, you do not gather the beauty of the flower."

Systems Thought

The concept of system as a fundamental structure of nature is not new. Bertalanffy traced it back to the beginnings of European philosophy:

> Philosophy was born when the early Greeks learned to view the world as a *kosmos* which was intelligible and hence controllable in thought and rational action. One formulation of this cosmic order was the Aristotelian worldview with its holistic and teleological notions. Aristotle's statement that "the whole is more than the sum of its parts" is a definition of the basic system idea.

But the holistic worldview was eclipsed in the sixteenth and seventeenth centuries by the Scientific Revolution, which was guided by the *metodo resolutivo* (resolutive or analytic method) employed in the brilliantly successful experiments of Italian astronomer-physicist Galileo Galilei (1564–1642). The analytic method of experimentation—learning how things work by literally or figuratively taking them apart to observe one element at a time—produced the major achievements of modern science and technology.

Because analytic experimental science replaced a holistic viewpoint that had originated in a metaphysical awe of the mysterious organizing force of the universe, most scientists of our time have equated all of science with analysis and have dismissed holism as a metaphysical antique. In contrast, Bertalanffy argued that *analysis is necessary but not sufficient*. He said there is an important dimension of existence that only manifests itself in wholes, a dimension that vanishes into thin air when the wholes are broken down into their isolated parts. It was his conviction, therefore, that modern science was generally engaged in a one-legged race for knowledge—running with analysis but without synthesis.

Bertalanffy realized, of course, that there are many persons in science and industry today who practice what is called systems science. But there is little agreement among them about what that term involves. To some, it means the application of computer systems to the storage and processing of information. To others, it means a method of analyzing a business procedure, such as the flow of paperwork in a particular department, by drawing a diagram. And to others, it means some combined use of data processing, diagraming, forecasting, inventory control, mathematical modeling, and simulation—often orchestrated by an interdisciplinary coordinator or multidisciplinary team of experts. The systems science *student*, Bertalanffy observed in 1968, often "receives a technical training which makes system theory (originally intended to overcome specialization) into another of the hundreds of academic specialties." Too often, he added, the word *system* is no more than "a fashionable verbal label."

Actual systems thinking is rare, very likely, because it requires that we place our thoughts in a new frame of mind, so that we think eclogically about everything under the sun. Systems thinking demands what Bertalanffy called "a change in basic categories of thought."

Most of us have been trained since childhood to think analytically, to confront our problems in a spirit of divide-and-conquer. Consequently, systems thinking requires that we pay attention to habits of thought that we ordinarily take for granted.

I don't want to give the impression, however, that such synthesis requires an effort that is in any sense superhuman. An important type of synthesis is performed by our brain automatically. We continuously organize great jumbles of incoming sensory data. If we didn't, we wouldn't be able to maneuver a car in traffic or a shopping cart in the super-market, and we would perceive television images as nothing but the dots of which they are composed.

Now, to illustrate what systems thinking is like, here's a relatively simple exercise in codebreaking that I've bor-rowed from a university course in problem solving. The coded message is:

MZQPQ LPQ AZQ XUCMX CT FQXAQPFQLP ?

If it looks hopeless, if you see no way to begin, you're probably looking at the parts rather than the whole. You're probably focusing on the individual letters or words rather than the entire sentence. If you view it as a whole, the first thing you'll notice is that it is a question. Inasmuch as questions commonly begin with words like WHO, WHAT, WHEN, WHERE, and WHY, you can guess that the first word, being five letters, is WHERE.

Now, go for the soft spots of the system. Try the second and third words rather than the ten-letter monster at the end. If the first word is WHERE, the next two words must end with RE and HE, as in ARE and THE.

Believe it or not, you now know enough letters to decipher the complete message, by engaging in a trial-and-error process in which you discard unpronounceable and other-wise unlikely words. The message, from fifteenth-century French poet François Villon's *The Ballad of Women of Olden Times*, is:

WHERE ARE THE SNOWS OF YESTERYEAR?

Note that you could not have begun to solve the problem by concentrating solely on its parts. The solution started to appear only when you focused on the whole and on the way the parts relate to each other to form the whole. That is the basic idea of the general systems approach.

Systems thinking understandably seems alien to most people because it commonly is associated with advanced mathematics, which does happen to be the principal language of GST research. Nevertheless, GST is a mental tool that is available to anyone—that is, anyone who is willing to make the effort of engaging in an unaccustomed manner of perception.

The General Systems Approach

Bertalanffy's general systems theory is a systems approach for all fields and all kinds of people, because it is a systems approach to problems in general.

As a consequence, his GST shows why man is so efficient about dealing with things and so inept about dealing with people, why we are geniuses in technology but ignoramuses in the realms of behavior and society. The answer, said Bertalanffy, is that we have consistently applied the systems insight about interaction to our machines but rarely to the basic goals of science, society, and self.

All of our technological marvels have been spawned by the insight that the characteristics of a system emerge not only from its parts but also and more importantly from the way the parts are arranged and the way they interact. Bertalanffy maintained that such insight could be applied with comparable success to the entire range of scientific, behavioral, and social questions. He therefore urged that we learn to "think interaction" in all aspects of our lives. If a marriage is in trouble, we must find a way to examine the marriage relationship instead of just examining one or both partners separately. If a child is in trouble at home or in school, we must somehow examine the child's interaction with his environment instead of just examining the child and the other involved persons separately. If a business is failing, we must examine the manner in which the failing entity is interacting with its environment, not just the nature of the business itself. If two nations appear to be heading toward war, we must examine the nature of their interaction as well as the nature of each nation separately. And so on, with any comparable example from any area of the human condition.

Bertalanffy advised his students that GST "points to new efforts and responsibilities." He explained that GST prescribes foresight rather than hindsight and crisis prevention in preference to crisis management. For example: whereas a technological systems approach focuses on the optimal design of an oil refinery, airport, shopping mall, or whatever, GST widens the scope of inquiry to ask if the project should be undertaken in the first place.

A technological systems approach was employed by the U.S. Defense Department for its military campaign in Vietnam. According to a *Fortune* article of January 1967, the systems analysts of the Pentagon deserved congratulations for "the best calculated military supply effort in twentieth-century U.S. history." As Bertalanffy frequently noted during the Vietnam era, a *general* systems approach to the Vietnam situation would have anticipated the ultimate failure of the U.S. military involvement by focusing on such non-military factors as Vietnamese history, culture, and nationalism, along with the morale of our fighting men in a war of such political and ethical ambiguity. Moreover, a Bertalanffian GST approach would have included the primary question of whether or not the U.S. should have made a military commitment in Vietnam at all.

The U.S. intervention in Vietnam was doomed, said Bertalanffy, because our government's systems analysts had failed to use one of the most important concepts of the general systems approach: *boundary definition.*

The purpose of boundary definition is to achieve a focus that is wide enough to include all factors that are relevant. Of course, you can't examine every problem in the context of the cosmos (Carl Sagan notwithstanding). Nevertheless, it is foolish to focus only on individual trees when there is a threat to the forest, or to focus only on the forest when there are environmental questions involving a whole economic system, or to focus on a single economic system when an issue involves the entire community of nations. A dedicated GST thinker is constantly aware of the boundary-definition problem of *suboptimization*, which means the failure to examine a sufficiently broad picture, as exemplified by a museum spectator who misses the significance or impact of a painting by standing too close.

Suboptimization occurs whenever anyone judges a book by its cover, public taste from TV ratings, an entire group from the actions of a few—or tries to predict the weather by looking out the window.

In a typical form of suboptimization, a politician may tell you that a certain criminal law in your state is harmful because the enactment of the law has been followed by an increase in crime. The factor missing from this judgment is the crucial question of what happened to crime elsewhere in the nation during the same period. Perhaps there was a nationwide crime wave, caused by something entirely different. Maybe this nationwide crime wave was much worse in other states, indicating that the aforementioned law in your state actually might have achieved relative crime control. By using your mind's eye to see beyond your personal horizon, you are applying an important aspect of the general systems approach.

The wide-angle view of GST can even benefit ecologists. They rightly pride themselves on their systems sophistication. They are deeply dedicated to revealing the interconnectedness of the web of life and the long-range systemic effects of reckless interference with the natural order. But ecologists might be better able to serve the cause of conservation if they adopted systems thinking that is general. GST might prompt ecologists to step back from their subject and discover that ecological issues can never be considered realistically in isolation from economics, just as economic development can never be considered realistically in isolation from ecology. From a Bertalanffian viewpoint, environmentalism can never be an issue unto itself; concern about the environment must be broadened to a concern about environment-plus-economics. Ecologists must become sensitive to questions about jobs and other bread-and-butter questions, just as the commercial sector must become sensitive to questions about clean air and water. Otherwise, no lasting progress will occur in either area. A case in point: the failure of ecologists to persuade Third World governments to halt the impending destruction of the world's two-and-a-half billion acres of rainforests. Some authorities believe half of that total area will be permanently destroyed by the year 2000 in the course of the Third World's expansion of fuel and farm development in response to their continuing population explosion. That would mean the loss of an enormous number of plant and animal species and perhaps a significant rise in global mean annual temperature that could trigger a whole series of worldwide ecological and economic disasters. In the words of Donald E. Stone, executive director of the twenty-four-university Organization for Tropical Studies: "It is impossible and probably highly undesirable to convince countries in which there is a high proportion of poor and hungry people to set aside lands for conservation purposes unless these efforts are linked with economic development that will improve their lot."

Humanistic General Systems Theory

Because Bertalanffy's general systems theory was truly general, it focused not only outward, on our world, but also inward, on our selves. This distinction became so significant that Bertalanffy eventually found himself being introduced to lecture audiences as the father of *humanistic* general systems theory.

Bertalanffy placed great emphasis on the need to view the human being as a system, with all that such a concept implies for mind-body unity and holistic medicine. He placed even greater emphasis on the human being as an open system, with all that such a concept implies for the interaction of our heredity and environment. And he placed his greatest emphasis on the human being as the ultimate expression of organized complexity, as a system with uniquely emergent qualities of creativity.

Bertalanffy's humanism markedly distinguished *his* systems approach from the technological approach of systems efficiency for its own sake. In Bertalanffy's GST, the social system must serve human goals, rather than vice versa. He believed that we must learn to live *with* systems—political, economic, technological, etc.—but that we ought never agree to live *for* such systems. That distinction, Bertalanffy warned, spelled the difference between human society and the society of insects.

His humanism was rooted in his belief in creative evolution. He was profoundly impressed with evolutionary evidence that the universal force of organization tends to move in the direction of increasing complexity, and that each level of complexity displays emergent qualities not present on the level below. As an exponent of evolutionary emergence, he vehemently opposed the reductionist view that living organisms can be completely reduced to explanations of physics and chemistry or that human behavior can be completely reduced to the explanations of biology. He contended that the repertoire of a rat is much greater than that of a robot and much less than that of a human.

Bertalanffy's opposition to reductionism was no mere academic technicality. He believed that our view of our self, our self-image, has a good deal to do with the way we behave and the way people behave toward us. A person who thinks he's nothing but a physico-chemical machine, Bertalanffy argued, is less likely to strive for human goals of fulfillment and dignity. A person who regards *Homo sapiens* as just another animal is less likely to cultivate human ideals of creativity and compassion.

In opposition to images of *Homo sapiens* as "the robot" of mechanistic technology, "the laboratory rat" of the behaviorist school of psychology, and "the naked ape" of pop anthropology, Bertalanffy put forward what he called a "new image of man," emphasizing the decisive role our species can play in shaping its own destiny. He based his new image of humanity on evidence that *Homo sapiens* creates an environment of its own out of symbols, and thus humans have the ability to direct their own evolution on ethical levels, through the cultivation of those symbols we call human values.

Because Bertalanffy's general systems theory was literally general, it took into account systems that are symbolic, including those of language, law, customs, values, and morality. For Bertalanffy, a system of beliefs was no less real or influential than a system of genes or glands. He therefore sought to raise our consciousness about the need to deal with our ethical beliefs as a system, an integrated whole, rather than as just a heap of maxims or a list of commandments. He contended that, when we thus integrate our moral philosophy, we arrive at a solution to the age-old question about using immoral means for moral ends. If our moral behavior is a systemic whole, then means and ends are one, just as mind and body are one when we view the human being as a system. In the spirit of the ethical precept of novelist-moralist Albert Camus (1913–1960)—"there are no ends, only means"—Bertalanffy's general systems theory holds that means and ends are identical.

That perception would seem to clarify the widespread dilemma of organized idealism, in which idealists create an organization to further their goals—in charity, religion, or social or political reform—then sacrifice the ideals on the organization's altar of expediency. A few years ago, for example, a famous charitable medical center raised some money for its treatment of lung-cancer and cardiac patients by allowing its name to be widely publicized as the beneficiary of a women's professional golf tournament that promoted the sale of a popular brand of cigarettes. The executive director of the medical center, who had devoted decades of his life to the center's laudable cause, adamantly defended the cigarette promotion during a long argument I happened to have with him about the matter. He summed up his defense by quoting, in Latin, the ancient motto, "There is no dirty money." Aside from the fact that he had misused the motto—which was originally uttered, it is said, by a Roman philosopher when someone upbraided him for earning a living as a cleaner of sewers—the medical center administrator had closed his mind to a wide-angle view of his moral position. Had he been trained in GST, perhaps he would have seen himself in the position of a man who attempts to fill a hole in his backyard by acquiring soil that he obtains by digging an adjoining hole.

A Bertalanffian view of society would tend to elevate social ethics by emphasizing the continual need to ask ourselves which level of the systems hierarchy is relevant for a particular ethical issue. For instance, a polluting industrial plant might be defended on the grounds that it provides prosperity to local workers, but a wider systems viewpoint would weigh that prosperity against the damage to the entire community and perhaps to future generations.

The Bertalanffian GST viewpoint is inherently ethical because it stresses an awareness of our functional interconnectedness with each other, with society, and with the environment we must all share. GST thus exposes the fragmented view of morality that permits a person to ignore the contradiction of being a saint on the job but a sinner at home, or a model head of a family who brings home bacon that has been stolen from another family.

On another level of behavior, a GST sense of ethics would end the fragmentation of our idealism. For example, civil rights activists might have saved themselves years of frustration if they had viewed busing as one factor in a social system rather than as a single end in itself. If busing advocates had backed up and looked at the larger picture, they might have empathized not only with the victims of segregation but also with the innocent bystanders of the middle class, whose children were being forcibly uprooted from their home environment by the busing program. Lacking a GST perspective, the busing advocates were temporarily successful in the small picture of partial racial integration but were sadly unsuccessful in the large picture of reforming the social system for minority children and the public in general. While winning integration battles, the busing advocates lost in wider arenas—as civil rights successes of the 1960s were undermined by middle-class political-economic backlash in subsequent years. Instead of busing children in an attempt to improve educational opportunities for the disadvantaged, the GST viewpoint suggests to this writer that a better answer might have been to bus dollars, as in moving some school funds from Beverly Hills to Watts. With that approach, the minority-neighborhood children might have received an upgraded education while families elsewhere continued to enjoy whatever value they placed on locally-based education for their children.

A New Worldview

Bertalanffy believed that the overall fate of the world depends on the adoption by humanity of a new set of values, based on a general systems *Weltanschauung* (worldview). He wrote:

> We are seeking another basic outlook: the world as organization. This [outlook] would profoundly change the categories of our thinking and influence our practical attitudes. We must envision the biosphere as a whole . . . with mutually reinforcing or mutually destructive interdependencies. [We need] a global system of mutually symbiotic societies, mapping new conditions into a flexible institutional structure and dealing with change through constructive reorganization.

In effect, Bertalanffy advocated a new patriotism. Like Patrick Henry, he believed that the time has come for us to widen our scope of allegiance. As patriot Henry dared to advocate that his people broaden their loyalty from state to nation, Bertalanffy advocated that we dare to broaden our loyalty from nation to globe. He urged that we become patriots of the planet, endeavoring to think and act primarily as members of humanity. Without necessarily diluting our own individual and cultural identity, he said, we must begin protecting the individual and cultural identity of others. He urged that we begin pledging our allegiance to humanity and to the earth on which we stand, one planet indivisible or no planet at all.

In his call for a universal declaration of interdependence, he advocated a new global morality: "an ethos which does not center on individual good and individual value alone, but on the adaptation of mankind, as a global system, to its new environment." The need for this new morality, he said, was imperative:

> We are dealing with emergent realities; no longer with isolated groups of men, but with a systematically interdependent global community. It is this level of [reality] which we must keep before our eyes if we are able to inspire large-scale action designed to assure our collective and hence our individual survival.

Human survival, in Bertalanffy's view, was the paramount purpose for cultivating the uncommon sense of general systems theory. He believed that the need for a general systems consciousness was a matter of life and death, not just for ourselves but also for what historian Arnold Toynbee computed to be 77,000 future generations that are possible on this planet before the death of our sun.

GST was likewise put forward as a mental tool for human survival in R. Buckminster Fuller's *Operating Manual for Spaceship Earth* (1969). In a chapter endorsing the GST approach, Fuller observed that humanity could no longer afford to ignore the fact that all of us on Earth are astronauts aboard a single spaceship system, and he concluded that we must begin immediately to view our situation in GST terms. Comparing humanity to an unhatched baby bird that has eaten all its readily available nutrient and must now break out of its shell to live, Fuller wrote: "We are faced with an entirely new relationship to the universe. We are going to have to spread our wings of intellect and fly or perish."

As geneticist C. H. Waddington wrote in his manual of systems thinking, *Tools for Thought* (1977): "The ways of looking at things that we have in the past accepted as common sense really do not work under all circumstances. We need nowadays to be able to think not just about simple processes but about complex systems."

As physician-author Lewis Thomas wrote in his collection of essays, *The Medusa and the Snail* (1979): "When you are confronted by any complex social system . . . whatever you propose to do, based on common sense, will almost inevitably make matters worse. If you want to fix something, you are first obliged to understand, in detail, the whole system."

As research pathologist W. I. B. Beveridge wrote in his testimonial to general systems theory, *Seeds of Discovery* (1980): "A basic reorientation of scientific thinking [is] needed to help us understand the essential nature of systems."

And as theoretical physicist David Bohm wrote in his book of essays on the philosophy of modern science, *Wholeness and the Implicate Order* (1980):

> The widespread distinctions between people (race, nation, etc.) which are now preventing mankind from working together . . . for survival [are largely caused by] the kind of thought that treats things as inherently . . . disconnected. So what is needed is for man to give attention to his habit of fragmentary thought, to be aware of it, and thus to bring it to an end.

In October 1931, fifteen months before Hitler became Germany's chancellor, English historian-novelist H. G. Wells (1866–1946) predicted that humanity's failure to adopt a global system of cooperation would result in the massive horror of a second global war. It was in that context that Wells issued his oft-quoted warning that civilization was losing "the race between education and catastrophe."

In the decades since that war, such warnings have become almost commonplace. Educator Robert M. Hutchins said "the world must unite or be blown to bits." Editor Norman Cousins said "the choice for the world's people is between being world warriors or world citizens." Naturalist Loren Eiseley saw humanity being confronted by its own "collective brain" with a choice between civilization's "last miracle or last disaster." And R. Buckminster Fuller saw us having to make the tantalizing/terrifying choice between "utopia or oblivion."

If we can avoid oblivion, a utopian future really is possible, according to some highly qualified sources. The world's leading authority on the origin of life, cosmo-chemist Cyril Ponnamperuma of the University of Maryland, advises me that he and certain colleagues could forever free humanity from hunger by establishing procedures for creating food through chemical synthesis and other new methods of unconventional food production. Ponnamperuma believes we have the basic knowledge. He says the job can be done if it is given an Apollo-like priority, with funds the superpowers could mutually divert from the arms race. Another scientist of great prominence in his field, University of Southern California Professor of Chemical Engineering Todd M. Doscher, tells me that scientists also have the know-how to solve the energy crisis. He says they can engineer environmentally safe methods of converting the global economy from oil to coal, which he believes would "buy us the one-to-two centuries needed to develop an ideal and permanent energy provider" such as nuclear fusion. Like Ponnamperuma, Doscher says the task he proposes can be achieved with funds the superpowers could mutually divert from the arms race.

The world's scientific community has abundant basic knowledge that can be applied to solve not only the prob-

lems of energy and food shortages but also those of over-
population and pollution, according to what I have been told
by geochemist Harrison Brown, one of the world's most
highly respected futurologists and director of the Resource
Systems Institute of the East-West Center in Honolulu:

> We can achieve a life for all humanity that actually
> would approach utopia. But what stands in the way
> is humanity's unwillingness to organize. We must or-
> ganize to end the arm's race, eliminate the gap be-
> tween rich and poor nations, and end the industrial
> world's lifestyle of economic waste. The urgent need
> for that organizational effort is the major problem that
> confronts civilization today. And, in the course of not
> taking those actions, humanity has put the world in
> a dangerous position whereby any one of a number
> of events can trigger a holocaust which would lead
> civilization to oblivion.

Oblivion or utopia? The *sane* choice demands that humanity adopt a wider perspective. We must learn to view our
species as a whole. We must learn to see the world as a
global system. In the same manner, on a personal level,
we must learn to understand how each of us interacts with
systems on all levels of our social existence, from our immediate family to the family of nations. As stated in
futurologist Alvin Toffler's *The Third Wave* (1980), we must
"move from a Second Wave culture that [has] emphasized
the study of things in isolation from one another to a Third
Wave culture that emphasizes contexts, relationships, and
wholes."

This present book is about that perspective, that vision,
that way of perceiving reality with the uncommon sense
of general systems insight, as conceived in uniquely profound detail by Ludwig von Bertalanffy.

The reader is invited to begin where Bertalanffy began,
with his work in biology, in which he developed his basic
systems concepts, including the model of the living or-

ganism as an open system. Then we'll see how he extended those ideas to current questions about evolution, the nature of human nature, the role of human values, the history and present status of human culture, and today's global threats to human survival. Next, we'll examine his proposal for a general systems discipline. We'll examine the multifaceted and multinational systems movement. And we'll conclude with his epistemological viewpoint of *perspectivism*, which reflected what he regarded as "the many flavors of truth."

All of this is preceded, however, by the story of Bertalanffy himself; for this book is also intended as an intellectual adventure story. On that level, it is the drama of a single human mind trying to comprehend the All. In Bertalanffy's seventieth-birthday *Festschrift* ("festival of writing" or anthology in tribute to a scholar), historian William M. Johnston of the University of Massachusetts wrote that Bertalanffy had strived "to integrate all aspects of experience." Like previous attempts to ascend the mountain of ultimate unity, this one failed to reach the summit. But there was triumph in the trying. Such attempts, regardless of outcome, affirm that our species really is special.

2

Professor von Bertalanffy:

WIZARD
IN DISGUISE

Bertalanffy was a true pioneer [and] he suffered a fate not unusual for pioneers: the full recognition of the validity and significance of his theories late in life or posthumously, and the subsequent reemergence of his original notions in different fields and forms, sometimes without reference to his earlier statements.

International Encyclopedia of the Social Sciences

H e was the Wizard of Oz in reverse. His wizardry was real, but he projected an image of the proverbial absent-minded professor.

At 70, teaching systems science and philosophy at the State University of New York at Buffalo, he was a short, portly, bespectacled gentleman who spoke slow and methodical English with a thick accent of his native Vienna. He peppered his lectures with self-deprecating humor. And he frequently entreated students to interrupt him with challenges: "Please do disagree with me *ja*? And if you decide to have a discussion, that is fine. You are my boss, you know."

In his private life, at the modest two-story home he shared with his wife on a quiet street in the Buffalo suburb of Williamsville, he seemed to live in the past. When he listened to music, from his record collection or on radio, his choice was Bach, Beethoven, Mozart, and Verdi. His hobbies were collecting ancient coins and Renaissance postmarks, and reading about Napoleonic history. He refused to own a television set or go to movies, preferring instead to look at slides of pictures he had taken of classic architecture during summer vacations in Europe.

He almost never drank. He went through the motions of dancing only at a few formal functions. He disdained parties, and he had no interest in parlor games like bridge. He refused to let his wife teach him her favorite game, chess, for fear that he would find it mentally distracting. What he did with his spare time—indeed, most of his time—was read, make notes, and write. He wrote notes before he rose from bed in the morning, intermittently through the day, and back in bed at day's end. Sometimes he would wake up in the middle of the night and write more notes.

But, hidden behind Professor Ludwig von Bertalanffy's fusty facade was one of the most exciting minds of the twentieth century. He was an intellectual adventurer who began his explorations where Albert Einstein feared to tread—the mysterious terrain of the living world—and who then proceeded to explore the realms of Einstein, Freud, Darwin and Descartes. He made a significant contribution to the reconciliation of science and the humanities, materialism and idealism, body and mind. He was an inter-disciplinary virtuoso, a polymath who proudly accepted the rank of fellow of the International Academy of Cytology (the study of cells), for his method of detecting cancer, and honorary fellow of the American Psychiatric Association, for his systems insights on mental illness. He could muster an uncanny diversity of reference points, and he could draw analogies that would never occur to thinkers whose exper-tise was limited to one or two fields. And from his generalist vantage point, he envisioned general systems theory, an approach to the full spectrum of human problems.

Though Bertalanffy was fascinated with the past, he was far from blind to the momentous events of his lifetime. Born eight months after the death of Queen Victoria, he saw civilization accelerate from horse-and-buggy to spaceship. He witnessed two world wars and two eras of economic collapse, the dismantling of the European empires, the rise and fall of the Third Reich, and the emergence of Marxism, Freudianism, feminism, the population explosion, birth control, aviation, electronics, mass media, atomic energy, plastics, antibiotics, frozen foods, radar, air conditioning, automation, computer science, and the preliminary stage of genetic engineering. He kept pace with such developments by speedreading newspapers, magazines and books of social analysis and criticism—meanwhile incorporating our past and present in his uncommon sense of what humanity must do in order to have a future.

Bertalanffy's Origins

In a sense, Bertalanffy's interest in history was something he was born into. The roots of the von Bertalanffy family tree—*ffy* means "son of," and *von* signifies nobility—could be traced back four centuries to the nobility of Hungary. In that *milieu*, coats of arms and charters proving noble rank were conferred typically for bearing arms with distinction to defend either of two rival Christian kingdoms against Moslem invaders from Turkey. Descendants of one such honored warrior of the mid-sixteenth century, Lieutenant Isaac Bertalanffy of the army of Rudolph I, included a long line of landlords. The Austrian branch of the family was founded by Charles-Joseph von Bertalanffy (1833–1912), who adopted the name Josef von Bertalan to pursue a career as a director of classical theater and operetta. His eldest son, Gustav von Bertalanffy (1861–1919), a prominent railway administrator, was the father of Ludwig von Bertalanffy.

When Gustav was thirty-four, he married Charlotte Vogel, a strikingly beautiful girl of seventeen. Charlotte, the daughter of a wealthy Vienna publisher, had been raised in upper-class Catholic schools subsequent to the death of her mother thirteen years earlier.

Charlotte von Bertalanffy bore a son who survived only

one week, then a daughter who died of complications of a throat infection at the age of two. Understandably, Charlotte became an unusually protective mother with the birth of her next and last child, born September 19, 1901, and Christened Karl Ludwig von Bertalanffy. Charlotte was so fearful that Ludwig might succumb to disease that she did not allow him to attend public school. He was educated by private tutors at home until he was ten, the age of entry into the *Gymnasium*, the nine-year European institution that combines what Americans call high school and junior college. Perhaps in part because of his private tutoring, Ludwig began school with so many academic advantages that he was able to pass his examinations with honors despite a poor class attendance record. His attendance record reflected his desire to study at home rather than spend time in class, and his continued home study tended to perpetuate his academic superiority.

About the time that he began school, his parents divorced. Both remarried, outside the Catholic church in civil ceremonies. Ludwig moved in with his mother and stepfather, Eduard Kaplan, who, like his father, was a prominent railroad administrator. Apparently the divorce was not traumatic for Ludwig. After an initial coolness toward his stepfather, Ludwig became friends with him and grew to appreciate his stepfather and mother's circle of friends, frequent houseguests who included artists, scholars, and scientists. Other frequent visitors, for Ludwig, were Ludwig's father and the father's new wife. Occasionally, Ludwig stayed with them, engaging in the same principal activity he performed at his new home: reading.

When Ludwig was seventeen, his father died. And that year, Austria suffered a serious economic decline. In the aftermath of World War One, with many Europeans fearing that the Bolshevik revolution in Russia would ignite uprisings in their countries, Ludwig's mother and stepfather hastily converted their real estate holdings into cash. Then postwar inflation caused the money to be drastically devalued.

A few years later, because of continuing hard times, Ludwig's stepfather was involuntarily retired with a pension.

Despite Austria's postwar decline, Ludwig had yet to experience any personal hardship. Vienna was still vibrant with opera, drama, concerts, and intellectual ferment; and Ludwig's pursuit of knowledge was undisturbed and undiminished. At the *Gymnasium*, he studied Homer, Plato, Virgil and Ovid in their original languages. He became familiar with the works of Lamarck, Darwin, Marx, and Spengler. He mastered calculus. On his own, he wrote poetry, a play about Cesare Borgia, and a novel he called *The New Tristan* (all to be consumed by the flames of the last days of World War Two). In a small home laboratory, he became adept with a microscope, while teaching himself dissection and animal and plant anatomy. Increasingly bored by classes, he eventually obtained permission to earn his graduation from the *Gymnasium* as a *privatist*, a student who attends school only for examinations.

Ludwig's early interest in biology was reinforced by the circumstance that his mother's suburban estate outside Vienna adjoined that of biologist Paul Kammerer (1880–1926). As a neighbor and family friend, Kammerer often discussed biology with Ludwig. (Kammerer is mostly remembered today because of Arthur Koestler's *The Case of the Midwife Toad*, a book about the scandal involving Kammerer's alleged doctoring of midwife toad specimens to win credibility for his supposed laboratory evidence of the inheritance of acquired characteristics. Kammerer reacted to the scandal by committing suicide.)

After a brief period at the University of Innsbruck, Bertalanffy enrolled at the University of Vienna, where he was equally attracted to science and philosophy and where he attended evening discussions of an internationally renowned group of scientists and philosophers known as the Vienna Circle. Under the direction of the Vienna Circle's founder, physicist-philosopher (and University of Vienna professor of philosophy) Moritz Schlick (1882–1936), the group met regularly to ponder scientific methodology and terminology in the spirit of *logical positivism*.

Logical positivism, an outgrowth of nineteenth-century French philosopher Auguste Comte's positivist philosophy that held that knowledge could only be derived from the "positive" data of experience and observation, branded as meaningless any concepts that could not be empirically verified. Consequently, logical positivists proposed that philosophy marry science and divorce metaphysics, thereby abandoning religion, ethics, and all questions of human values.

Though Bertalanffy admired Professor Schlick personally, and grieved when Schlick was shot to death by a deranged student, Bertalanffy became a lifelong and vocal opponent of logical positivism. As such, he commonly reminded his readers and lecture audiences that he had participated in the Vienna Circle, by which reminder he made the point that his opposition stemmed from first-hand knowledge of "the limitations of this philosophic attitude."

He indicted the logical positivist attitude for *scientism,* the dogmatic view that science (particularly physical science) is the only key to reality. He also attributed to logical positivism the view of science in which experimentation is everything and theory is nothing. In contrast, he liked to quote the Kantian maxim that, though theory without experience is mere intellectual play, experience without theory is blind. Bertalanffy never tired of arguing that the great accomplishments of science have been the product of observation inspired by theory. Above all, Bertalanffy opposed the logical positivist edict that scientists must restrict themselves to what *is* and eschew all questions about what *ought* to be. Bertalanffy contended that every scientific endeavor is biased by the original decision to engage in that particular endeavor, and that a denial of the existence of such fundamental bias amounts to hypocrisy or moral idiocy. He held that absolute scientific objectivity is a myth, and that scientists who really have no interest in human values are *de facto* robots.

An Unusual Courtship

As a trim and attractive young man, Bertalanffy had two memorable encounters with the opposite sex. The first involved a raven-haired Italian girl whom he studiously avoided discussing in later years, apparently never revealing how they met or why they had gone their separate ways. But the relationship must have been a memorable one, judging from the fact that he acknowledged learning from her how to read and speak Italian, and that he kept a collection of her love letters as a permanent part of his personal library.

The other woman in his life was a blonde and fragile beauty named Maria Bauer. She was a Viennese businessman's daughter who had been graduated from a *Gymnasium*, had passed the Austrian qualifying examination for entering a university and was considering a career in mathematics or medicine. But, as she was to recall many years later, "I never did go on to the university, because my career became Ludwig."

Indeed, she became part of him. The story of Ludwig von Bertalanffy became the story of Ludwig and Maria from the time of their first meeting. Not one of his accomplishments from that point on was untouched by her.

They met in April 1924, when Ludwig was twenty-three and Maria was twenty. She was recovering from a six-month siege of the frequently fatal Spanish grippe, and her family's doctor had suggested to her parents that they send her for further recuperation to a skiing resort in the town of Kufstein in the Austrian Alps. When she arrived there by herself at the train station, she was greeted by young Bertalanffy (who was walking with a cane, because of a ski injury). He explained that the resort's porter was unavailable because the skiing season was over, and he was filling in as a favor to the resort's owner, his mother.

"And, if you'll permit me to introduce myself, I'm Ludwig von Bertalanffy."

"But how were you able to find me among all the people getting off the train?"

"Simple! You were the most intelligent-looking!"

His compliment was distinctly Bertalanffian, considering the type of compliment other young men would pay an attractive girl, then and now. At any rate, his next statement left no doubt that his interest in this resort guest was more than a matter of routine courtesy.

"Instead of taking the car, let's walk. I'll have your suitcases picked up, and we can have a nice stroll for about twenty minutes."

So they strolled and they talked. They continued to talk at dinner, and they were almost never apart for the next forty-eight years.

About their courtship, Maria recalled: "Our first meetings weren't typical for young lovers. You know, young people talk mostly about love and things like that. But although we also talked about love, mostly we discussed articles that Ludwig had been writing. On the second day, he had me read the manuscript of an essay he had sold to a German newspaper literary section on the subject of Oswald Spengler's recently published *Decline of the West*—so he could discuss it with me. Then there were other essays of his to discuss with me: on Goethe, on Hieronymous Bosch and some modern painters, on mysticism, and so on. A few days after we met, he took me somewhere for a dance. I really liked dancing at that time, but Ludwig was so bad at it that I asked him to please never take me dancing again. . . . Looking back on our early days together, I realize I must have fallen in love with his brain. You know what I mean? His intelligence. And that was fortunate for me, because if you fall in love with the brain of someone, you cannot become bored. A person's intelligence stays attractive forever."

Maria recuperated at the Kaplan resort from April until September, during which time she also got to know Ludwig's mother and stepfather. When she returned to Vienna, Ludwig frequently visited her and befriended her father,

who began referring to Ludwig as "the walking en-
cylopedia."

Ludwig and Maria were married March 1, 1925. At first
the newlyweds lived with Maria's father—her parents were
separated and heading for divorce—and then the young
couple moved to a three-room apartment near the University
of Vienna.

Maria now began her career as helpmate to Ludwig von
Bertalanffy. She cooked, cleaned, and budgeted. And she
became his lifelong chauffeur and typist, with Bertalanffy
justifying his refusal to learn how to drive and type by
quoting the nineteenth-century Austrian statesman Metter-
nich to the effect that a creative person should devote himself exclusively to the things that only he can do rather
than spending time on things than others can do.

"Ludwig wasn't lazy," Maria insisted. "He simply refused
to take time from his reading, thinking, and writing. In
our beginning years, when we sometimes went hiking in
the mountains, he always had paper and pencil. Even if
we'd go for a walk, he'd end up behind me, writing something on a paper. He'd do the same thing when we had
company. All his life, if something came to his mind, he
wrote it down. I think his brain was always working."

And thanks to Maria, his brain did not have to work
alone. Maria effortlessly adjusted to Ludwig's professional
ego. While typing a manuscript, if she found something
she didn't like, she never proclaimed her disapproval. Instead, she turned her objection into a diplomatic question:
"Ludwig, do you think it might be clearer if you said it
this way?" On major issues, she generally refrained from
giving advice until Ludwig requested it, as he did on a
memorable occasion shortly after their marriage, when he
told her he was having trouble deciding if he should become
a biologist or a philosopher. She replied: "I think you'll
be better off in biology, because biologists are more in demand. And a biologist can use what he knows to be a
philosopher, but it cannot work the other way around."

(Maria described herself to me as a believer in women's

rights, "including the right to choose the role that I played." She said she never regretted having devoted her life to her husband's career. And her self-portrayal of contentment in the marriage was confirmed by many individuals who encountered "Mutzi" and her "Lutzi"—their pet names for each other—through the years. A psychologist friend of theirs recalls: "I have never seen such total devotion of one person to another. She filled a very important role, and there was joy in her commitment.")

A week short of their first wedding anniversary, Maria bore their son, Felix, who, by choice, was to be their only child. Ludwig now sometimes dictated his writing to Maria with Felix astride his shoulders or riding piggyback. When Felix was three, Ludwig taught the child to identify the national origins of postage stamps in Ludwig's collection. Later, Ludwig frequently lectured the boy about the wonders of nature. When Felix was ten, Ludwig bought him a microscope and showed him how to see the invisible creatures in pond water.

Meanwhile, Ludwig was ascending the professional ladder. In 1926, with physicist-philosopher Schlick as his mentor, he earned his doctorate with a thesis about the pioneering psychophysics of physicist-philosopher Gustav Fechner (1801–1887). In 1928, Ludwig published *Kritische Theorie der Formbildung (Modern Theories of Development: An Introduction to Theoretical Biology)*. In 1932, he published the first volume of *Theoretische Biologie (Theoretical Biology)*. In 1933, his *Modern Theories of Development* was translated into English by English philosopher of biology Joseph Henry Woodger. The following year, the University of Vienna named Bertalanffy a *Privatdozent*, a faculty lecturer with prestige but no pay. He earned his living entirely from his writing for a year or so, until he went on the payroll as a professor in the department of zoology, where he taught biology to medical students.

In 1937, he was awarded a Rockefeller Foundation fellowship to spend a year studying American developments in biology for possible application to his courses in Vienna.

Leaving Felix in the care of Ludwig's mother and stepfather, the Bertalanffys headed first for a stay at the University of Chicago. As a Rockefeller fellow, he lectured as well as listened, and a Bertalanffy lecture at a philosophy seminar there became the occasion for his first public advocacy of a science to seek and apply laws of systems in general. From the University of Chicago, in the spring of 1938, Ludwig and Maria took off for a cross-country lecture tour. For the Bertalanffys, this was the best of times and the worst of times, as they gloried in the sights of the Rockies, the Grand Canyon, and the Northern California redwoods, and as they learned that their homeland had been swallowed up in Hitler's *Anschluss*.

Ludwig and Maria decided to remain in the United States, at least for a while, with the intention of sending for Felix as soon as they settled their plans. Ludwig chose the most likely course: an application for a year's extension of his Rockefeller fellowship. But that plan was thwarted by a Catch 22: a representive of the Rockefeller Foundation advised Ludwig that his application required a letter from his university guaranteeing that Ludwig would still have a position to return to after the second year of the fellowship. Ludwig quickly obtained the letter and submitted it with his formal request for the renewal. According to Maria's recollection, the foundation responded something like this: "Dear Professor von Bertalanffy: Judging from your application, you will have no trouble resuming your work at the University of Vienna. But, as you must know, there are many scholars and scientists who have no position to return to because of the European political situation. So we must regretfully reject your request in order to help those with greater need." The Bertalanffys appreciated the moral logic, but their disappointment nevertheless ran deep.

Bertalanffy received one alternate offer. An American colleague at the University of Chicago offered the Bertalanffys the hospitality of his farm if they chose to defect and then arrange somehow for a continuation of Ludwig's career. But Ludwig could not bring himself to accept a proposal with that much uncertainty. He decided to gamble on the future in Vienna. He spent the remainder of his fellowship, June to October 1938, at the Marine Biological Laboratory in Woods Hole, Massachusetts, where he conducted flatworm experiments on the nature of growth and had a chance to discuss his biological theories with several other biologists, including Paul Weiss and Thomas Hunt Morgan. Then he and Maria boarded a ship at New York for their reluctant return to Europe. Though they were anxious about the future, they did not guess that they were sailing toward the maelstrom of World War Two.

War Years

Upon his return to Vienna, Bertalanffy plunged into his work. Because of his stature as the author of two major books on biology, a publisher in Germany offered him the founding editorship of the *Handbuch der Biologie (Handbook of Biology)*, a fourteen-volume encyclopedia with about seventy contributing authorities. Bertalanffy undertook the job with staff support consisting entirely of Maria and her typewriter.

At his University of Vienna laboratory, Bertalanffy continued his investigations into the nature of growth, including the abnormal growth of cancer. After war broke out, in the fall of 1939, he undertook an unusually heavy teaching load: as a lecturer on biology for medical students, he suddenly encountered auditorium-packing classes of more than a thousand as a result of a ruling that a youth could avoid being conscripted into the German army by enrolling as a student of medicine.

Bertalanffy had a somewhat subversive record under the Third Reich, as the author of a 1930 essay, *The Science of Life and Education*, which denounced biological theories that seemed to justify racism. Maria was told that copies had been destroyed in a Nazi bookburning. Bertalanffy also had a reputation for provoking between-classes arguments with Nazi sympathizers on the university faculty. And, if the authorities had wanted to check, they could have discovered that he and Maria had been close friends before the *Anchluss* with a certain Professor Joseph in the university's zoology department, a Jew who committed suicide with his wife when the Germans entered Austria. Maria had had an even closer Jewish friend, an old schoolmate named Felicitas Mond, who was taken away with her mother to a concentration camp in Poland, where she was presumed by Maria to have died in a gas chamber.

Despite those associations, the Bertalanffys suffered no government harassment. Throughout the war, the Germans granted scientists a slack leash, perhaps because the ranks of Third Reich scientists had been seriously depleted by the persecution and flight of Jewish scholars.

The Bertalanffys' only wartime fears, therefore, were of the war itself. They grew to dread the sound of the cuckoo, because that was the signal, broadcast on the radio, of an impending air-raid. The Bertalanffys also were worried about the possibility that Felix would be drafted, but he managed to avoid active military service by serving the last ten months of the war in a medical corps station on the outskirts of Vienna.

The most difficult part of the war, for the Bertalanffys, occurred at its conclusion. In April 1945, during the Russian siege of Vienna, they had to find temporary shelter elsewhere. After the siege, when they made their way back home through rubble and corpses, they found a smouldering wreckage where their apartment building had stood. Their neighborhood had been destroyed by German flame-throwers as part of the Nazi policy of scorched-earth retreat.

In Maria's recollection: "We had lost everything that connected us with the past: our library of about 15,000 volumes and every possession acquired during some twenty-five years. Worse still, the work of many years was destroyed, including the major part of a sequel to *Theoretische Biologie*. Silently, we took each other's hand and went to the university. There Ludwig registered at an emergency office. As it turned out, he was the only professor left in the zoology department. We went upstairs. Although no actual fighting had taken place there, Ludwig's office and laboratory had been destroyed three months earlier by a bomb, and the entire department was in shambles and ransacked. The only alternative was between despair and work. Six weeks later, Ludwig and a couple of office assistants had the department functioning again, in time for the 1945 summer semester."

During the next three years, living in a small furnished apartment, the Bertalanffys contended with the problem of sheer survival. Many of their neighbors routinely went to farmers to trade radios, furniture, and other possessions for food to supplement the near-starvation rations that the occupation government allowed the populace. The Bertalanffys had nothing to trade, and most of Ludwig's university salary went to the black market to satisfy Ludwig and Maria's craving for cigarettes and coffee. They survived nutritionally as a result of CARE parcels sent by friends in England and America, with the CARE wrappings doing double duty as fuel to keep them warm during the fierce winter of 1946. Ludwig managed to pay for their rationed food and their rent by selling weekly popular-science articles to a Vienna newspaper, *Der Kurier* (*The Courier*), with illustrations drawn by Felix. Eventually, Bertalanffy also contributed to scientific journals, and he began to work on two books, a biology text for medical students, which he never completed, and *Das Biologische Weltbild* (*Problems of Life*), which was to become one of his major works.

Postwar Odyssey

Problems of Life, subtitled *An Evaluation of Modern Biological Thought*, was the Bertalanffys' ticket out of the desolation of postwar Vienna. In 1948, a publisher in Bern, Switzerland, invited them to come there so Ludwig could devote full time to the task of completing that manuscript. The three of them left Austria with the legal maximum of ten Swiss francs, but they were able to live fairly comfortably at a

Bern hospice because the publisher gave them advance royalties. Their future, however, was quite uncertain. Just before departing for Switzerland, Bertalanffy had been told by a friend that the occupying Soviet forces had placed him on a blacklist because of his biological publications in opposition to the then-prevailing Marxist-Leninist dogma of Lysenkoism (a belief in the inheritance of acquired characteristics). With their political bridges apparently burned behind them, the Bertalanffys once again were aided by a sympathizer from another country. This time their rescuer was the English biologist Woodger, who had become an admirer and friend as a result of having translated *Modern Theories of Development*. Woodger, the head of the biology department at the University of London Medical School's Middlesex Hospital, arranged for Ludwig to serve an academic year there as a visiting professor. (Felix, lacking a position in England and therefore unable to get a visa, stayed in Switzerland to become a lab assistant to a pulmonary surgeon in Zurich.)

Bertalanffy was delighted to be a colleague of Woodger—delighted to spend hour upon hour discussing with him the views they shared about the phenomena of life. But no day passed for Ludwig during the following eight months of 1948–1949 without worry about where he and his family would go at the end of the Middlesex appointment. Once again, a rescue came in the nick of time, in this instance from the Lady Davis Foundation, which had been organized to bring European scholars to Canada. With Felix joining them so he could earn a Ph.D. in anatomy from McGill University in Montreal, the Bertalanffys sailed to their new life aboard the *Empress of France*. Ludwig was assigned the first few months to McGill, then to the University of Ottawa to serve there as a professor of biology and as director of research at that university's newly established faculty of medicine. He again taught biology to medical students, he created a biological research department, and he secured government grants to finance his work on growth and cancer. One of his laboratory technicians, assigned to the task of operating on cancerous rats, was a squeamish but dedicated $1500-a-year employee named Maria von Bertalanffy.

It was at the University of Ottawa that Bertalanffy began a series of experiments that eventually culminated in the Bertalanffy Method of cancer cytodiagnosis (cell diagnosis) and research. Those experiments were part of his pioneering investigation of the physiology of animal cells by means of the fluorescence microscope, an early twentieth-century Viennese invention that uses ultraviolet illumination in combination with fluorescent dye. Bertalanffy observed that one such dye, acridine orange, causes an animal cell's DNA (deoxyribonucleic acid) to glow green but makes its RNA (ribonucleic acid) fluoresce quantitatively in shades of reddish brown to brilliant orange or fiery red, depending on the quantity of RNA in a particular cell. Thus, a cell's orange or red glow under the fluorescence microscope indicates unusual amounts of RNA, which suggests that RNA is performing excessive amounts of protein synthesis. This in turn signifies an abnormally intense metabolism and growth of the cell, which indicates the possibility of cancer. What all this added up to in Bertalanffy's mind was a simple method of cancer screening that could be performed by any physician in the ten minutes it takes to prepare a cell sample of a body secretion. In more than ninety percent of the cases, the orange or red warning-signal would be absent, which would mean that the patient could be dismissed as "negative." Only the remaining cases would require an examination of their morphological cell structure by a trained cytologist to determine if there were a need for a biopsy.

Also at the University of Ottawa, Bertalanffy's long years of growth research bore fruit. Having observed growth in bacteria, insects, rodents, worms, snails, and fish, he developed mathematical equations that could be used to predict a given species' growth rate on the basis of that species' rate of metabolism. The Bertalanffy Growth Equations were adopted as a method of yield-forecasting by a number of the world's fisheries, including those of the British Ministry of Agriculture and Fisheries and also the fisheries of the Food and Agriculture Organization of the United Nations. Elsewhere, the equations were applied in botany, animal husbandry, and basic research on the growth process.

And so, Bertalanffy's reputation grew; and he extended it further by translating his *Problems of Life* into English and by using English as well as German in his numerous scientific papers.

In 1952, he was invited to go on an eighteen-university lecture tour in the United States. Because he was two years shy of the residency requirement for Canadian citizenship, he had to apply to the U.S. consulate for a visa. At the consulate, he encountered an unexpected problem. An official there asked him to explain why his bylines had appeared in a Soviet-backed Vienna newspaper (*Der Kurier*) after the war. Bertalanffy replied that freelance writing had helped pay for groceries and rent during those difficult days, and that the articles were not political but strictly scientific, and that in any case he could hardly be considered an agent of the Kremlin. His explanation apparently didn't help, probably because the U.S. then was under the dark cloud of McCarthyism. Shortly before his scheduled departure for the lecture tour, he received a letter informing him that his visa had been denied. According to Maria: "Ludwig got mad. And I got really mad. I went to the consulate and demanded to talk with the consul. I said to him, 'How would it look for the U.S. government when we write letters to eighteen universities and tell them why the U.S. is forbidding a distinguished scientist from lecturing to them?' I warned the consul that somebody was bound to publish the story. I can't remember exactly what I said word-for-word, except that I was very angry. And I must have made an impression, because Ludwig a couple of days later received a notice that his visa had been approved."

Bertalanffy went on the tour without Maria. Had she gone with him, as the keeper of his itinerary, she might have spared him an unforgettable embarrassment. Having been in correspondence for some time with Aldous Huxley—each was a fervent admirer of the other's contribution to modern thought—Bertalanffy eagerly accepted an invitation to attend a party in Bertalanffy's honor at the Huxley home in Los Angeles. Many luminaries attended, including Igor Stravinsky. But, alas, not Bertalanffy. He mistakenly flew to Los Angeles one day late. Mr. and Mrs. Huxley ended up having to give a second party for one guest: Bertalanffy. Nevertheless, the Huxley-Bertalanffy relationship continued unabated in person and in correspondence until Huxley's demise in 1963. They frequently sent each other their latest writing, each responding with praise and encouragement.

Back at the University of Ottawa, Bertalanffy grew restless. He found himself in the frustrating position of being honored as a distinguished member of the international scientific community while being taken for granted at his rather modest and peripheral home base. In 1954, as a consequence, he took a considerable professional risk. A few days after receiving his Canadian citizenship, he quit his Canadian job in response to an invitation to become a founding fellow at the Ford Foundation's Center for Advanced Studies in the Behavioral Sciences at Stanford, California. (Felix remained in Canada to conduct cancer research in an academic-scientific career that continues today at the medical college of the University of Manitoba in Winnipeg.) Ludwig's decision was fateful for the systems movement, because it was at the Center that he joined forces with economist Kenneth Boulding, biomathematician Anatol Rapoport, and biologist Ralph Gerard in conceiving the Society for General Systems Research. But Center appointments lasted only one year. Ludwig had to become a job-seeker again, at the age of fifty-four.

He landed his next job from another Center fellow, psychiatrist Franz Alexander. Dr. Alexander, the renowned pioneer of psychosomatic medicine, had accepted an offer to establish a Psychosomatic Research Institute at Mt. Sinai Hospital in Los Angeles (now Cedars-Sinai Medical Center); and Alexander invited Bertalanffy to join him as co-director in charge of biological research (effective November 1955).

Bertalanffy lost no time writing Huxley about "the great news." At the hospital, Bertalanffy conducted studies of hallucinogenic and tranquilizing drugs used in psychiatry, and he continued his research on physiology and cancer diagnosis. In 1956, he published a report on his "Acridine Orange Fluorescence Method of Cytological Cancer Detection." Despite the deterrent expense of fluorescence microscopes and their consequent rarity in doctors' offices, the Bertalanffy Method was adopted as a screening technique for many types of malignancies by cancer laboratories in America and abroad. The method, proven clinically on specimens from more than ten thousand patients at son Felix's lab at the University of Manitoba, also was widely adopted for laboratory research, including biochemical studies in virology and embryology. The Bertalanffy Method was hailed by scientific and medical directors of such organizations as the National Cancer Cytology Center of New York and Miami, Hospital Pirovano in Buenos Aires, and the Institute of Molecular Biology of the U.S.S.R. Academy of Sciences in Moscow.

During his period at Mt. Sinai Hospital, he held a concurrent appointment as a visiting professor in the department of physiology at the School of Medicine of the University of Southern California. The position paid no salary, but it gave him a chance to remain active in teaching, in this case as a lecturer to psychiatric residents. He also gave lectures at the Hacker Psychiatric Clinic in Beverly Hills, at the invitation of its founder, Vienna-born psychoanalyst Frederick J. Hacker. In addition, Bertalanffy continued his role as a public speaker. He went to Monterey to participate in a symposium of the Western Psychological Association. In San Francisco, he presented a paper on human nature to the Northern California Psychiatric and Psychosomatic Societies. And he voyaged to Geneva for a World Health Organization symposium on "The Psychobiological Development of the Child," with Swiss developmental biologist Jean Piaget, anthropologist Margaret Mead, ethologist Konrad Lorenz, and psychoanalyst Erik Erikson.

In Los Angeles, he and Maria lived in an attractive, Spanish-style house about three miles from the hospital. These were happy years for them, but the period was all too brief. In 1958, the Mt. Sinai Hospital research project and the hospital experienced financial difficulties. Once again, Bertalanffy had to find a job.

As before, he dictated a series of employment-seeking letters to Maria. And, as had become usual in recent years, she attempted to persuade him to use the face-saving approach of first having colleagues make inquiries on his behalf. But he stubbornly refused to solicit such help, perhaps because of the wounded pride that can be gleaned from the following comment he made to a lecture audience during this phase of his life: "While universities go desperately hunting for junior scientists and can never have enough of them, seniors are left in the lurch because, as the routine phrase goes, 'Unfortunately we have no place for a scientist of your reputation, experience, caliber, and superior achievements.'" Bertalanffy's senior status may not have been his only handicap as a job applicant. According to two of his colleagues, some members of the academic establishment were prejudiced against him because he had returned to Austria after the Hitler annexation.

Boulding recalls that Bertalanffy never confided in people like him about job insecurities: "If he had, some of us would have made an effort to get him a good, steady position. At least I would have tried to get him into the University of Michigan, where I was then. I don't think anybody of my acquaintance ever knew the difficulties he was in."

Bertalanffy obtained his next position from Karl Menninger. Dr. Menninger, who had recognized the value of Bertalanffy's systems approach to psychiatry, invited Bertalanffy to spend the next couple of years at the Menninger Foundation in Topeka, Kansas. Once again, Bertalanffy was given the title visiting professor, and he occupied himself by giving lectures and seminars for Menninger staffers.

By the time that appointment ended, with Bertalanffy now nearing sixty, he was offered a position from another admirer in behavioral science. This invitation came from psychologist Joseph R. Royce, who had first learned of Bertalanffy's work by reading several of his papers on systems theory, and who had befriended him when both were working in Los Angeles. Now Royce was a professor of psychology at the University of Alberta in Edmonton, Canada, and he wanted Bertalanffy to help him launch the university's Center for Advanced Study in Theoretical Psychology. To provide a suitable academic niche for Bertalanffy, Royce arranged a joint appointment for him as a member of the Center and as a professor of theoretical biology in the department of biology. But Royce's principal motivation was to have Bertalanffy join him as co-teacher of a Center seminar on theoretical psychology and the philosophy of science.

Bertalanffy was more than happy to accept. He wrote Huxley: "I have been invited to serve as a sort of professor at large without definite teaching obligations but with connections with several departments. I hope that I can use this time to write at least some of the books which, in the form of illegible notes and drafts, are slumbering in drawers." During the Edmonton years, 1961–69, Bertalanffy published *Robots, Men and Minds* (1967) and *Organismic Psychology and Systems Theory* (1968), the first an edited and the second a verbatim version of a pair of talks he gave in 1966 at Clark University in Worcester, Massachusetts; and he published a collection of his scientific journal articles, *General System Theory* (1968), which was translated into German, Italian, French, Spanish, Swedish, and Japanese. He initiated a correspondence with London-based Arthur Koestler . . . —Bertalanffy wrote Koestler: "reading your books, I feel I'm conversing with a kindred spirit"—and the two became friends in person at a summer science conference in Alpbach, Austria.

Bertalanffy's professional overseas trips included one to Germany to give a series of lectures sponsored by the Reimers Foundation for Anthropogenic Research and another to the Soviet Union to lecture about his method of cancer diagnosis at an International Cancer Congress in Moscow.

And he was one of the honored guests invited from Canada by the U.S. government to attend the presidential inauguration of Richard M. Nixon. The inauguration was historic on two counts of which President Nixon was unaware: Professor von Bertalanffy wore a tuxedo, and he joined Maria in what passed for a dance.

Back on the Edmonton campus, Bertalanffy indulged his love of interacting with students. The feeling was mutual, to judge from his crowded classes and the approximately thirty students who jammed the Bertalanffy living room one night a week to attend a non-credit seminar. The university administration twice invited him to remain for an additional year after he reached their retirement age of sixty-five. But, after receiving those extensions, he accepted a teaching position at the State University of New York at Buffalo, where the official retirement age was seventy.

Final Years

At SUNY Buffalo, Bertalanffy was appointed to the Faculty of Social Sciences but assigned to the Center for Theoretical Biology, where he gave various courses on systems science and philosophy. A typical Bertalanffy course title: "Science, Society, and Culture." A colleague at the Center, mathematical biologist Robert Rosen, recalls: "Though Bertalanffy was not prepossessing physically, he was quietly extroverted and gregarious, and he had no hesitancy about approaching people he didn't know. Once embarked on conversation, which with him was almost instantly, all else tended to be forgotten. And, despite the ungodly hour that he chose for his three-hour seminars—four o'clock on Friday afternoons, when almost everyone was anxious to scramble away for the weekend—he never had fewer than fifty people, most of whom returned week after week."

Early in 1971, Bertalanffy had a mild heart attack that caused his doctor to confine him to Buffalo's Kenmore Mercy Hospital for three weeks of rest. His comments upon returning to class, in a course called "Perspective Philosophy and the New Image of Man," further indicate the rapport he had with his students: "Now, you see, I am back. I must thank you for the welcome-back inscription on the blackboard. And I have to thank you most warmly and cordially for the many notes you were good enough to send me at the hospital. You know, being in the hospital is not precisely fun. Though I have never been to prison, it seems to me that the difference is not great, apart from the fact that usually you don't go to prison with a heart attack. So it was really not only most welcome but encouraging to me that you sent all those nice notes. I am particularly grateful that some of you have written to tell me that there is a human relation between us, and that I have in a small way given you something. That is the greatest compliment, you know, that a teacher can receive. I was really moved and touched. Thank you so very much."

In September 1971, Bertalanffy reached SUNY's retirement age but was granted another year's extension. On the occasion of his seventieth birthday, September 19, an interdisciplinary symposium was held in his honor by the philosophy department at the SUNY campus at Geneseo. Participants included Boulding, Rapoport, Rosen, and GST philosopher Ervin Laszlo.

On a Friday morning, June 9, 1972, with the university summer vacation underway, Bertalanffy was working in his upstairs study, writing notes. Shortly before noon he was stricken with a second heart attack. Maria summoned an ambulance, and he was taken back to Kenmore Mercy Hospital, this time to the intensive care unit.

Maria spent most of the ensuing weekend at the hospital, usually in the waiting room, sometimes beside his bed, occasionally talking with him when he was up to it. In her recollection: "When they let me in to see him Sunday night at eight, he seemed fresh and alert. He told me he had been scheduled to attend a meeting at the university on Wednesday, and he asked me to call someone the next morning to explain why he would be absent. He then told me about several other things he was supposed to do, and he asked me to contact people about those matters. It was very nice for me to see him so alert, even though my visiting allowance that time was only fifteen minutes. Then I went home to get some sleep. Shortly before one o'clock in the morning, I got a call from a neighbor, a man who had been helping me in this emergency. He said the hospital wanted him to drive me back there. At the hospital, they informed me that Ludwig had died shortly after midnight."

When Maria left the hospital that time, she wore two wedding rings.

Bertalanffy's body was cremated. (In the only comment he had ever made to Maria about the eventuality of his death, he had asked for cremation "rather than a lot of fuss.") An intimate memorial service was conducted at the funeral parlor by a Catholic priest who had attended some of Bertalanffy's seminars, Father Chris Puehn. Participants included colleagues and family, the latter consisting of Maria, Felix, and Felix's wife, Gisele. Bertalanffy's ashes were interred at a cemetery in Montreal (home of Gisele's family), beneath a black marble gravestone bearing Bertalanffy's name, the years of his life, and the von Bertalanffy coat of arms.

Felix and Gisele remained a month to be company in the Buffalo house for Maria. She chose to continue living there for the rest of her life, and she continued to some extent to serve as Bertalanffy's editorial assistant. She helped compile and edit two book-length collections of his articles, *Perspectives on General System Theory* (1975) and *A Systems View of Man* (1981). And she maintained Bertalanffy's personal files for the use of visiting researchers.

Meanwhile, recognition for Bertalanffy proceeded posthumously. Two systems-science anthologies, *The Relevance of General Systems Theory* and *Unity Through Diversity*, were published in Bertalanffy's honor. The latter was a two-volume *Festschrift* with contributions from sixty-three authors in thirteen countries. The Society for General Systems Research initiated a Ludwig von Bertalanffy Memorial Lecture for their annual meetings. (And, as Maria subsequently learned, Bertalanffy had been nominated for a 1972 Nobel Prize in physiology.)

Though Bertalanffy had not wanted any posthumous "fuss," Maria told me that he probably wouldn't have minded my selecting the following lecture-fragment of his for a biographical epitaph:

> [In] tribute to that slightly ridiculous figure, the professor: Our society certainly keeps him in his appointed place in the human pecking order. He definitely ranks below . . . second-rate television starlets, fashion models or boxers. . . . However, he has a secret vengeance. . . . It is we who, in the last resort, manufacture the glasses through which people look at the world and at themselves—little as they may know it. . . . I dare say we are the great spectacle makers in history.

3

The ABCs of GST:

CONFRONTING THE RIDDLE OF LIFE

Bertalanffy's roots were solidly anchored in the theory of biological systems, of which he initiated some of the deepest pioneering studies. From these roots grew unique insights into the character of social and behavioral systems, as well as the creation of a general systems theory which bound all these activities together into an integrated intellectual edifice of unique amplitude and power.

> Biologist Robert Rosen's
> Bertalanffy Memorial Lecture
> at the 1979 meeting of the Society
> for General Systems Research

General systems theory—as a holistic way of thinking based on an awareness of the behavior of systems in general—might have germinated in just about any field. It got started in biology because that's where its father, Ludwig von Bertalanffy, got started.

GST became an intellectual mansion of many rooms, with Bertalanffy's contributions to biological theory serving as the foundation. His biological concepts inspired his general systems insights in physiology, medicine, psychology, psychiatry, sociology, history, education, and philosophy.

And, because Bertalanffy was a biologist with his heart

in philosophy, his GST acquired an intellecual richness it might not otherwise have developed. GST became not only an objective tool of thought but also a worldview: a humanistic-systems alternative to the mechanistic values sanctioned by the Industrial Revolution.

As someone who lived and breathed philosophy, Bertalanffy never regretted having chosen a career in biology, the science of life. He saw biology occupying the central position of knowledge, based on physics and chemistry, and in turn the basis of the behavioral and social sciences. More importantly, because biology focused on what he called "the riddle of life," he regarded his occupation as a uniquely fertile source of clues to fundamental philosophic questions:

Is life some chemical combination that happened by accident? Is living matter nothing more than temporarily animated dust?

Are we the result of a random toss of genetic dice? Or are we the product of a universal pattern or purpose?

If there is a pattern or purpose, do we have any free will in the matter? Or are we only flesh-covered machines that have been programmed to perform according to a script we have no capacity to understand, much less change?

Those questions would seem to have an urgent relevance today. With humanity now technologically capable of fashioning its own future, or denying itself any future at all, the philosophic view we have of life and of our own species may well affect the most important decisions in all history.

Human behavior, Bertalanffy taught, depends to a significant degree on human values. How we act depends largely on whether we love things and use people, or vice versa. How our leaders act depends largely on whether or not we cultivate a society in which—to quote Ralph Waldo Emerson (1803–1882)—"things are in the saddle, and ride mankind." Though few of us take time to philosophize, all of us practice one philosophy or another in behavior reflecting social values that are so ingrained that we tend to take them for granted. Our most basic values, Bertalanffy was

In summary, he observed that "the acceptance of living beings as machines, the domination of the modern world by technology, and the mechanization of mankind are but the extension and practical application of the mechanistic conception."

Among the forebears of contemporary mechanistic thought in biology, Bertalanffy identified the most influential as the founder of modern philosophy, French philosopher-mathematician René Descartes (1596–1650). Descartes said all of nature was just matter in motion according to mathematical laws, and every organism was a *bête machine* (mechanical beast). Descartes attempted to reconcile his science with his Catholic faith by declaring that all these machines were created by God and that God had made the human machine unique by giving it a soul. Bertalanffy delighted in telling his students about Descartes, because cartesian mechanism seemed to be a blatant admission that the mechanistic approach was such an inadequate explanation of life that it could only be saved by divine intervention—a *deus ex machina*.

Even the father of mechanism in physics, British physicist Sir Isaac Newton (1642–1727), combined his view of the universe as an immense machine with a belief that the machine was created by God.

Nevertheless, the mechanistic viewpoint primarily appealed to pure materialists. A notable example cited by Bertalanffy was French physician-philosopher Julien Offroy de La Mettrie (1709–1751), who employed Descartes' concept of *bête machine* in an atheist manifesto called *L'Homme-machine*, in which La Mettrie illustrated the link between biological theory and ethical philosophy by proclaiming: "We are no more committing a crime when we obey our [machine-like] instincts than the Nile is committing a crime with its floods."

For Bertalanffy, the epitome of mechanistic absolutism was a famous pronouncement by French astronomer-physicist-mathematician Pierre-Simon de Laplace (1749–

1827). Laplace declared that total knowledge of the laws of physics would reveal the future of every particle and every person; and free will was thus an illusion:

> Given for one instant an intelligence which could comprehend all the forces by which nature is animated and . . . sufficiently vast to submit those data to analysis—it would embrace in the same formula the movements of the greatest bodies of the universe and those of the lightest atom: for it, nothing would be uncertain and the future as the past would be present to its eyes.

Biological mechanism became dominant along with the development of modern science. Beginning with the early seventeenth-century discovery by British physician William Harvey that the heart functions as a blood-circulating pump, one biological phenomenon after another appeared to yield to mechanical explanations. Limbs were likened to levers, the eye became a camera, the brain became a switchboard, and human consciousness became nothing but the motion of molecules. In the mechanistic metaphor of evolutionary biologist Thomas Henry Huxley (1825–1895), father of Julian and Aldous, humans were "conscious automata."

Today's most influential approach to life science is molecular biology, an offspring of genetics and biochemistry that seeks to understand biological phenomena in terms of the molecules within the cell. Today's prevailing biological viewpoint is the *reductionist* position that all biological phenomena can be reduced in explanation to phenomena that are strictly mechanical. According to this view, all existing biological mysteries are just mechanical questions awaiting mechanical answers. A typical expression of that approach appeared in the introduction to *Biology and the Future of Man* (1970), a book-length report issued by the National Academy of Sciences under the editorship of biochemist and NAS president Philip Handler (1917–1981):

Living phenomena are indeed intelligible in physical terms. And although much remains to be learned and understood, and the details of many processes remain elusive, those engaged in such studies hold no doubt that answers will be forthcoming in the reasonably near future.

Bertalanffy acknowledged that mechanistic biology had been responsible for major achievements, notably in bio-medical research and genetics. But he steadfastly denied that mechanism could answer all of life's questions. He stipulated that some biological phenomena are machine-like in their passive response to the environment. But he ar-gued that other biological phenomena are completely un-machinelike in the sense that these phenomena are initiated from within. Life is a considerable step higher than nonlife, he insisted, because life not only reacts but also acts. In that regard, he concluded, life can never be fully explained by the laws of physics and chemistry.

Life's challenge to mechanism, Bertalanffy wrote in his *Modern Theories of Development*, is vividly clear in the living embryo:

Of all the wonders which life presents to us in such plenty, that of development is surely the greatest. Let us recall what it means: on the one hand we have this little drop of jelly which, as a fertilized ovum, represents the germ of an organism; on the other is the wonderful edifice of the complete living creature, with its myriads of cells, its endlessly complicated organs, characters, and instincts. When we compare the beginning with the end of this process, it is easy to understand why it is that in all attempts to solve the great riddle of life, scientifically or philosophically, this cardinal problem of development has been pre-ferred as the starting point.

The mystery of embryonic development will always defy mechanistic science, Bertalanffy declared, because embryonic development is simply not mechanical. Likewise, he continued, mechanistic science will never satisfactorily explain the ability of living things to violate the law of *entropy* (the Second Law of Thermodynamics), which dictates that all physical events move from a condition of available energy to unavailable energy (as occurs when coal is burned) and move from the improbability of order to the probability of disorder (as occurs when high tide erases a sand castle). In the physical world, clocks unwind, batteries wear out, champagne unfizzes, hot dogs become cold, and every star in the sky eventually vanishes like a bar of soap in a tub of water. Contrariwise, in the realm of life, organisms act like coal that burns without burning up or like windup clocks that keep rewinding themselves. From embryo onward and upward through evolution, biological entities flout the law of entropy by exhibiting *negative entropy* (*negentropy*), the tendency toward increasing order and complexity, the movement from formlessness to form.

Another major embarrassment to the mechanistic theory of life, said Bertalanffy, is the biological phenomenon of *equifinality:* the ability of organisms to reach a given final goal from different initial conditions and in different ways. (In non-living systems, the final state and the means to that state are fixed by initial conditions.) He and other biologists used that term to identify the organism's inner-directed ability to protect or restore its wholeness, as in the human body's mobilization of antibodies and its ability to repair injured skin and bone. The most dramatic form of equifinality is regeneration: lizards regrow lost tails, salamanders regrow lost limbs, and common garden worms regrow lost heads. If a flatworm is cut into a number of pieces, each can develop into a normal individual. If a living sponge, which is a plant-like animal, is squeezed through a piece of cloth and thereby separated into its constituent cells, the cells will slowly regroup and restore the original creature.

The classic laboratory demonstration of equifinality was performed by German developmental biologist Hans Driesch (1867–1941) in the course of his study of the sea urchin, a creature commonly used in biological research because its embryonic cell divisions are easy to observe. Driesch divided sea urchin embryos in half by separating the two cells formed by the embryo's first division. Each half developed into a whole creature, though slightly undersized. The same thing happened when he divided the embryos in quarters and eighths. Conversely, when he fused early-stage embryos, the pair grew into a single whole organism, though slightly oversized. Driesch's equifinality demonstrations, confirmed by the experiments of other scientists, have worked on frogs, newts, and many other animals. And we now know that the same phenomenon occurs spontaneously in humans, when divided embryos produce identical twins.

Laboratory experiments by Caltech neurobiologist Roger Sperry, a 1981 Nobel laureate prize winner, have shown that toads, salamanders, and other amphibians exhibit an uncanny equifinality in their optic nerve. If the nerve is severed, it regenerates and then acts as if it has a mind of its own about plugging itself back in the site it had occupied in the brain. If the experimenter blocks the nerve with a physical obstacle, the nerve takes whatever detour is necessary to reach its destination. If blocked completely, it will plug in elsewhere and subsequently shift to its intended position if the route becomes unobstructed.

Bertalanffy saw equifinality as proof that organisms pursue inner-directed goals. He said organisms are goal-seeking in the sense that they exhibit what he called purposeful behavior to maintain their condition or achieve their intended condition. He thus linked biology with *teleology*. Teleology, the explanation of phenomena by reference to some ultimate end for which a thing or event is believed to be produced, is regarded by most modern biologists as a subject for metaphysics rather than science. As far as they are concerned, a purpose presupposes a mystical entity that is directing the action. In the candid words of a nineteenth-century German physiologist, Ernst Wilhelm von Brücke (1819–1892), "Teleology is a lady without whom no biologist can live; yet he is ashamed to show himself in public with her." Bertalanffy, however, repeatedly embraced teleology in public. And, instead of shame, he displayed vehemence: "If teleology represents an essential feature of reality, then science must take account of it."

Before Bertalanffy, biological teleology had been generally associated with the theory of *vitalism*, which held that organisms are directed from within by a soul-like or spirit-like vital force. That theory was expounded by Aristotle (384–322 B.C.), and it dominated biological thought until the middle of the nineteenth century. Aristotle identified the vitalizing force as an entity called an *entelechy*, meaning "that which bears the end in itself." Subsequent vitalist philosophers called the animating imp by other names—*anima*, *monad*, and *psychoid*—but the term *entelechy* was reintroduced by the most recent major exponent of vitalism, embryologist Driesch. Though he was an outstanding scientist, the best definition he could devise for his entelechy was "something in the organism's behavior which shows that the living organism is greater than the sum or an aggregate of its parts." Neither Driesch nor any other vitalist was able to say anything more definite about their invisible agent of animation. Vitalists simply said it had to exist, because they could not imagine any other explanation for the fact that some forms of matter exhibit inner-directed behavior and others don't.

Though Bertalanffy's criticism of mechanism was identical to that of the vitalists—and consequently, his position was described by some writers as vitalistic—he regarded vitalism as a theory that led to an intellectual dead-end:

> Vitalism must be rejected as far as scientific theory is concerned. According to it, structure and function in the organism are governed, as it were, by a host of goblins, who invent and design the organism, control its processes, and patch the machine up after injury. This gives us no deeper insight; but we merely shift what at present seems inexplicable to a yet more

mysterious principle and assemble it into an "X" that is inaccessible to research.

A New Standpoint

In response to what Bertalanffy deemed the intellectual sterility of vitalism and the dogmatic nothing-but-ism of mechanism, he proposed "a new standpoint":

> This view, considered as a method of investigation, we shall call "organismic biology," and as an attempt at explanation, "the system theory of the organism." Every organism represents a system, by which term we mean a complex of elements in mutual interaction . . . . In one brief sentence, [this *organismic conception*] means that organisms are organized things and, as biologists, we have to find out about it.

In effect, he advocated a scientific effort to rescue life's uniqueness from the mechanists, who denied it, and from the vitalists, who obscured it with mystification. As opposed to mechanism, Bertalanffy's new standpoint depicted life as an emergent level of reality and therefore as only partly explainable by physics and chemistry. As opposed to vitalism, Bertalanffy's new standpoint did not attribute life's uniqueness to poltergeists but to biological laws. Instead of describing the factor that makes organic wholes greater than the sum of their parts as an entelechy, which cannot be scientifically studied, he described life's vital factor in terms of systems relationships, which can be scientifically studied.

Because organisms are wholes rather than heaps, Bertalanffy believed that a proper scientific study of them demanded not only an investigation of their isolated parts but also an investigation of the whole system in operation. No matter how carefully and how often you dissect a frog, he maintained, you can never fully determine why it behaves like a frog. You must also observe the actual coordination of its parts and processes. Likewise for dissecting an ox or an orchestra, a gnat or a nation. Bertalanffy's organismic conception, in effect, was scientific extrapolation of an observation made by poet William Wordsworth (1770–1850): "We murder to dissect."

Orchestrating everything in life, said Bertalanffy, is an organizing force: "The problem of life is that of *organization*." For him, the conventional term for a living entity, *organism*, could not have been more appropriate. In Bertalanffy's organismic view, the visible essence of an organism is not its substance but its form, because form is the expression of organization. Organisms are "charged with form," Bertalanffy wrote in *Modern Theories of Development*, "the way batteries are charged with electricity."

Bertalanffy pondered life's organizing force on all its levels, beginning with the level of the cell (which had been recognized as the basic biological unit since the early nineteenth century). He considered the living cell "a superlative complex organization" that could never be totally understood by the study of its molecules. He said we must study how it works: within each cell is a complete industrial system, organized in a complex of warehouses, assembly plants, power stations, and processing plants—with highways for transport of raw materials and the export of manufactured protein and waste. He was profoundly impressed by the systematic organization within living cells, and also by the organization among cells in an organism. To mechanists, biological organization is merely evidence that life is mechanical. To Bertalanffy and other exponents of *organicism*, (the organismic conception), life's organized complexity deserves at least as much attention as scientists would give to the discovery of a factory on Mars.

He regarded the living organism as the quintessential system because the parts and the whole exist in a state of total reciprocity. The whole depends on the parts, and the parts depend on the whole. An organism dies if crucial parts die, and all parts die if the organism dies. Living systems abide by the motto of the Three Musketeers, "All for one, and one for all."

In his effort to focus scientifically on the riddle of life, Bertalanffy was among those who pioneered the concept of living entities as *open systems:* systems functioning beyond the limits of conventional physical chemistry. He began using that term in 1932, in the first volume of his *Theoretische Biologie,* to designate systems that maintain their dynamic existence by continuously exchanging matter and energy with their environment, as animals import oxygen and food and export carbon dioxide and nitrogenous wastes. By contrast, he classified nonliving systems as *closed systems,* (in effect, isolated from their environment), except for special cases such as rivers and flames. Though Bertalanffy was not the first to use the open-system concept, and though the concept was a statement of self-evident facts, his use of the idea was a major achievement because he turned it into an extremely versatile tool of thought. In Bertalanffy's mansion of general systems theory, the concept of the open system became a key that opened many new doors of insight, not only in biology but also in behavioral and social science.

In biology, he described equifinality and other aspects of inner-directed activity as basic open-system characteristics. That may at first sound like begging the question—substituting the open system for the entelechy—because he did not shed any new light on the puzzle of why life behaves the way it does. However, he earned himself an important place in the history of biological thought by proclaiming that the mysteries of life are a proper study of science, so long as the scope of inquiry is pointed away from the scientifically unanswerable *why* of life and toward the *how.* The mysteries of life are characteristics of open systems, he said, so let us begin studying life in the perspective of that model.

He proposed, for example, to apply the open-systems model to a scientific study of life's negative entropy:

In open systems we have not only production of entropy due to irreversible processes, but also import of negative entropy. This is the case in the living organism which imports [consumes nutrients with] complex molecules that are high in free energy. Thus, living systems, maintaining themselves in a steady state, can avoid the increase of entropy, and may even develop towards states of increased order and organization.

Bertalanffy published this idea in 1940, thereby becoming the father of the *thermodynamics of open systems*. He later wrote that he considered it one of his most important accomplishments. And he proudly cited the subsequent studies in this field by Austrian physicist Erwin Schrödinger (1887–1961), who made the oft-quoted observation that "what an organism feeds upon is negative entropy," and the Russian-born Belgian physical chemist Ilya Prigogine, whose development of the thermodynamics of open systems was to win him a 1977 Nobel Prize.

In the discipline of biology, meanwhile, Bertalanffy remained the foremost open-systems pioneer. On all levels of life, from cell to biosphere, Bertalanffy saw open systems being maintained by "the continuous flow of matter." In that respect, he frequently quoted Greek philosopher Heraclitus of Ephesus (*circa* 540–480 B.C.): "Everything is in flux. . . . You cannot step into the same river twice, for fresh water is forever flowing towards you." Bertalanffy extended the Heraclitean image to the far reaches of human conceptualization by postulating that life is not just *in* flux; it *is* flux. "Living forms are not *in being*," he wrote, "They are *happening*. They are the expression of a perpetual stream of matter and energy which passes through the organism and at the same time constitutes it."

Consequently, Bertalanffy maintained, biologists should stop thinking of their discipline in terms of two distinct fields: *morphology* (the study of organic structures) and *phys-*

iology (the study of organic processes). Instead, he proposed that biologists think in terms of what he called *dynamic morphology*, signifying that morphology and physiology are different approaches to the same phenomena: "What are called structures are slow processes of long duration; functions are quick processes of short duration. [In human terms:] We believe we remain the same being, but in truth hardly anything is left of the material components of our body in a few years; new chemical compounds, new cells and tissues have replaced the present ones."

Thus, he said, we constantly change while maintaining an illusion of permanence that Bertalanffy called a *steady state*. This dynamic concept of life was applied by Bertalanffy to all organisms—"It is the essence of metabolism"—and to all levels of biological organization. The idea of the open system's steady state, maintained by a self-regulating balance of decay and synthesis of building and energy-yielding substances, became another of Bertalanffy's fruitful organismic-systems concepts. He wrote: "This [self-regulating steady state] is the fundamental mystery of living systems; all other characteristics such as metabolism, growth, development, reproduction, autonomous activity, etc., are ultimately consequences of this basic fact."

Significantly, when he introduced the steady state concept of biology while still writing solely in his native German, he had to coin a tongue-twister for it, *Fliessgleichgewicht* (flow equilibrium), because the German language had a term only for *stationary* equilibrium. Bertalanffy felt he needed that new word to spell out the active quality of the steady state as compared with the passive quality of conventional physico-chemical equilibrium. For the same reason, to avoid the static connotation of the word *equilibrium*, Harvard physiologist Walter Bradford Cannon (1871–1945) had introduced the term *homeostasis* (in 1932). That was Cannon's coinage for the self-regulation of such conditions as body temperature and blood sugar for the purpose of maintaining a relatively constant internal environment in response to changes in external environment—a phenomenon previously explored by French physiologist Claude Bernard (1813–1878).

Bertalanffy regarded the concept of homeostasis as a useful description of much "goal-directed" biological behavior. But, at the same time, he expressed concern that the concept could be used to justify a mechanistic view of the organism as "nothing-but" an entity that responds to output monitored back as input to regulate future output:

> Although the homeostasis model transcends older mechanistic schemes by acknowledging goal-directiveness in self-regulating circular processes, it still adheres to the machine theory of the organism. . . . The feedback model is essentially the classical stimulus-response scheme [with] only the feedback loop being added. However, an overwhelming amount of facts shows that primary organic behavior is spontaneous.

He was aware, of course, that organisms including us frequently act in response to stimuli. But he believed that the stimulus-response behavior of organisms is preceded in early development by activity that is purely spontaneous, which he construed as evidence that active behavior is biologically primary and that reactive behavior is secondary. In support of that view, he cited inner-directed swimming patterns of paramecia [single-celled protozoans] and studies of spontaneous behavior among "embryos and fetuses of various species, from axolotls [a type of Mexican salamander] to birds to humans." He further cited evidence of playful activity among animals as well as playful and creative activity among humans.

Bertalanffy believed that it was crucial to his philosophy and science of life to recognize that "the organism is not a passive automaton reacting to stimuli but rather is an essentially and autonomously active system." Recognition of that fact, he said, was enormously important in all areas of human relations.

Alongside the open system, Bertalanffy placed a second basic model of general systems thought: *hierarchical order*. Reality, in Bertalanffy's worldview, is a tremendous hierar-

convinced, originated with notions about the question towards which all others in biology converge: the nature of life.

If our view of life inspires awe, said Bertalanffy, we will tend to treat life with reverence, and we will tend to treat each other with respect. But, he said, most of us have no such view of life, because we are products of a modern *Zeitgeist* of machine-worship. And he believed that our society's machine idolatry was responsible for and reinforced by the prevailing biological theory of *mechanism:* the viewpoint that all living entities, including humans, are nothing more than complex machines.

A Voice Against Mechanism

Bertalanffy spent a lifetime denouncing mechanism as a doctrine that was scientifically unjustified and morally degrading. In 1928, reflecting on the technologically efficient carnage of World War One, he warned that the machine was dragging humanity "down to its own level." He repeated that warning through subsequent wars and the current race to prepare the ultimate machines of efficient destruction for World War Three. He further warned that mechanistic attitudes had seeped into virtually every area of social behavior, encouraging doctors to view patients as cases, employers to regard workers as units, advertisers to regard consumers as stimulus-response robots, and television programmers to reduce the public to a set of demographic numbers. He saw the human individual being reduced to the cardboard image described in magazine journalist William H. Whyte's *Organization Man.* He saw human society being reduced to what social critic Lewis Mumford identified as the mechanistic social order: the *Megamachine.* And, in the late 1960s, he told lecture audiences in Europe and America that he "envisioned with horror" the possibility that mechanistic biologists would use genetic engineering to pursue the Hitlerian dream of creating a super-race.

chical architecture of organized entities—wheels within wheels, to use the image of the cosmos projected by the prophet Ezekiel. In the perspective of modern physics, there is the hierarchy from atom to solar system to galaxy to universe. In biology, there is the ladder-like order of life: atoms form molecules which form compounds which form the chemical building blocks of cells which form completed cells which form tissues which form organs which form organisms. The organisms form communities which form ecological systems which ultimately form the whole biosphere.

Hierarchical order may seem obvious—the subject isn't even discussed in many textbooks of biology—but Bertalanffy and other systems thinkers believed in this instance that too many of us have yet to open our eyes to the *implications* of the obvious. Organismic-systems thinker Arthur Koestler (1905–) called the subject "an old hat [that] can produce lively rabbits."

Systems in hierarchical order, to use terminology introduced by Koestler, are *holons* (from the Greek *holos* for "whole," with the suffix *on*, as in neut*ron* or prot*on*, suggesting "a part") or *Janus-faced entities*, by which terms Koestler meant that they are wholes when facing downward and parts when facing upward. Each of these systems is a whole in relation to its parts and a part in relation to a superordinate whole. A systems hierarchical view, therefore, sees the individual human being as both an autonomous entity and also as a member of social systems that unavoidably impose restraints on that autonomy. In Koestler's *The Ghost in the Machine* (1967), he defined the "well-adjusted person" as an individual who has achieved an approximate balance of a "self-assertive tendency" to behave selfishly and an "integrative tendency" to behave in accordance with one's dependence on society. He added that the search for properties or laws that all types of hierarchies have in common should be a priority for the general systems discipline proposed by Bertalanffy.

Bertalanffy's model of hierarchical order was furnished by him with four related concepts: As life ascends the ladder of complexity, there is *progressive integration*, in which the parts become more dependent on the whole, and *progressive differentiation*, in which the parts become more specialized. In consequence, the organism exhibits a wider repertoire of behavior. But this is paid for by *progressive mechanization*, which is the limiting of the parts to a single function, and *progressive centralization*, in which there emerge leading parts (like the brain) that dominate the behavior of the system.

Those biological concepts, Bertalanffy suggested, may be extended to systems in general. As an example, he cited the fact that evolution of society from primitive to industrial stages has brought many advantages but only at the cost of progressive mechanization and centralization, which pose serious problems of vulnerability. A disruption in a leading part can disrupt the whole system. Bushmen have no air conditioning but also no power failures; their routines of life cannot be interrupted by a technical crisis such as the blackout that paralyzed thirty million people in nine states and three Canadian provinces on the night of November 9, 1965. Perhaps a study of these concepts for systems in general would help us determine the full price of a technological or social innovation before we commit ourselves to it.

Bertalanffy believed that the organismic hierarchy extended beyond cells, organs and organisms to "a world of supra-individual organizations." In fact, he pointed out, there is a continuum bridging the realm of organisms and supra-individual organizations. In the fuzzy border between the two categories are rigidly organized colonies of creatures such as those that form the venomous jellyfish called the Portuguese Man-of-War; and there are insect societies in which the function of the specialized members is so rigidly specified that the society resembles an organism. To a limited degree, he said, the organismic analogy may be applied to societies of humans. And, foreshadowing the ecological consciousness that emerged in America in the 1970s, he focused on "the still higher systems of animal and plant communities, ecosystems in which the disruption of a part jeopardizes the whole."

His writing on biological communities inspired some early members of the European forest conservation movement, who applied Bertalanffian ecological thinking to the development of the idea of the *dauerwald* (perennial forest) as an alternative to uncontrolled and reckless exploitation of timberland.

He also pioneered the view that the whole of life on Earth can be regarded in some ways as a single organism. He thus inspired today's image of Earth as a single biosphere, reminding us that actions anywhere on the globe can bring reactions anywhere and everywhere. For example, if we continue to burn fossil fuels indefinitely and without adequate exhaust controls, say some authorities, there will be a buildup of carbon dioxide in the atmosphere, trapping heat radiating off the Earth's surface, resulting in the melting of polar icecaps and the flooding of many of the world's coastal cities. In that scenario, nobody will know how much carbon dioxide is too much until too late.

Bertalanffy perceived a hierarchy of ecosystems, such as lakes, forests, and regions. And, though there is a struggle for existence within an ecosystem between plants and animals and between animal predators and prey, the ecosystem maintains a steady state. However, Bertalanffy warned that such a natural balance can be jeopardized by our careless interference. He cited the notorious example of DDT, which was highly effective in killing insect pests but which entered the food chain so that it also killed wildlife and ended up in human tissue and mother's milk all over the world. (Though the U.S. banned DDT in 1972, that insecticide continues to be widely used in Mexico and elsewhere, and the remaining insecticides in the U.S. are of questionable long-range effectiveness in view of the equifinal ability of insect species to produce strains resistant to the poisons they encounter.) Bertalanffy endorsed the systems-ecological answer of maintaining each ecosystem's steady state by emulating its natural population controls. He believed that society should increase its currently tiny investment in nonpoisonous pest-control research, so we can improve safe techniques such as the sterile-male method, the use of growth-inhibiting hormones, and the introduction of natural predators like the roundworms that kill fruitfly pupae.

Bertalanffy endorsed the ecological viewpoint, expressed by GST philosopher Ervin Laszlo, that our role in nature should be a partnership that inspires both humility and pride. As Laszlo explained in his *The Systems View of the World* (1972):

> The systems view of nature and man is clearly non-anthropocentric, but it is not nonhumanistic for all that. It allows us to understand that man is one species of system in a complex and embracing hierarchy of nature, and at the same time it tells us that all systems have value and intrinsic worth.

Organismic Evolution

The organismic-systems viewpoint, as pioneered by Bertalanffy, also had profound scientific and philosophic implications for the theory of evolution.

The Darwinian revolution, like the Copernican revolution that had dethroned the Earth and put our planet in its place as a modest sphere orbiting a modest star among myriad stars, has been interpreted by many thinkers as a shattering blow to humanity's pride. If we are just another animal, produced by random forces of nature, then are we wasting our time to dream about the human potential and human destiny? Are all philosophers, poets and artists nothing but pretentious primates?

Bertalanffy found renewed justification for human pride—and a renewed justification for a sense of wonder about the mystery of life—by viewing the biological drama of evolution through the lens of the general systems viewpoint. Where orthodox evolutionists saw fatalism, he saw hope. Where they saw chance, he saw natural law. Where they saw determinism, he saw free will.

The trouble with most evolutionists, he said, is that they are mechanistic. He identified the mechanistic view of evolution with *neo-Darwinism*, or what Julian Huxley called the *Modern Synthesis:* a synthesis of modern genetics with the theory of natural selection advanced by naturalist Charles Darwin (1809–1882). Bertalanffy disputed neo-Darwinism during most of his career. One of his last university lectures was devoted to a criticism of French molecular biologist Jacques Monod's *Chance and Necessity* (1970), a book-length essay in defense of the neo-Darwinist position that all forms of life evolved as a result of "chance" mutations and the "necessity" of Darwinian selection.

Bertalanffy granted that natural selection and random mutations played a role in the evolutionary process, but he rejected the assumption that they accounted for the whole story. He argued that necessity could not explain nature's apparent diversity-for-the-sake-of-diversity: for example, why the cow finds it necessary to have a complicated multiple stomach while another vegetarian creature of roughly the same size, the horse, survives quite nicely with its simple stomach. Bertalanffy knew that neo-Darwinians point to all existing adaptations as successful survival mechanisms, but he dismissed that argument as nothing but a tautology: "The selectionist explanation always is a construction *a posteriori* [after the fact]. Every surviving form, structure, or behavior [is declared to be] of some selective advantage. But this is no proof that it was a product of selection."

Bertalanffy also doubted that natural selection and random mutation could produce strikingly complex biological systems like the human eye, with its automatic lens and its retina of 130 million light-sensitive rods and cones. The chance of that happening, he contended, was about the same as the possibility that nature would randomly produce "a race of grandfather clocks." Darwin had anticipated that challenge by arguing that amazingly complex entities could evolve during the long stretches of evolutionary time. Bertalanffy's response to that *gradualism* argument was to question how the first primitive organ of sight could have randomly appeared, considering that a partially evolved organ of sight (like a partially evolved wing) would have had no survival advantage, and random mutations would have been much more likely to destroy rather than improve whatever potential value the unfinished eye (or wing) might have had.

Regardless of the eventual scientific verdict on such questions, Bertalanffy believed that neo-Darwinism would never be able to explain the overall evolutionary phenomenon of evolving complexity, the progression from simple to complex organisms. That trend in nature—which Bertalanffy called *anamorphosis*, a term he borrowed from a contemporary German biologist, Heinz Woltereck—was the rock on which Bertalanffy stood in his opposition to neo-Darwinism. If survival of the fittest were really the basic theme of evolution, he pointed out in all seriousness, then today we should all be microbes.

Inasmuch as evolution kept ascending beyond the microbe, he said, a force other than natural selection must have been operating. He identified that force as the organismic-systems principle of organization.

Bertalanffy's alternative to mechanism in evolution, the organismic-systems approach, involved a search for natural laws of organization, laws of systems, that can explain the gaps left by neo-Darwinism:

> From the standpoint of general biology, the fundamental issue of evolution is not the origin of species. It is the origin of organization. . . . The origin of new species means a readjustment of organization at almost all levels. Thus it appears that we have to look for organizational rules characterizing their changes. . . . I believe the discovery of these laws constitutes one of the most important tasks of the future theory of evolution.

In a sense, Bertalanffy was echoing Darwin himself, who had confided in his private correspondence that he had "an inner conviction" that the universe was not the result of chance. Darwin wrote that he was "inclined to look at everything as resulting from designed laws."

Among post-Darwinian thinkers, French philosopher Henri Bergson (1859–1941) wrote in his *Creative Evolution* (1907) that evolution is an expression of an *élan vital* (vital impulse) which continually creates new biological forms. South African statesman-philosopher Jan Christiaan Smuts (1870–1950) examined the philosophic aspects of evolution in *Holism and Evolution* (1926). For Smuts, holism was "a synthetic tendency in the universe, and is the principle which makes for the origin and progress of wholes in the universe," culminating in mind and personality. French Jesuit paleontologist Pierre Teilhard de Chardin (1881–1955) posited an "ascending energy" in the cosmos, leading to all higher entities. In Father Teilhard's posthumous testament, *The Phenomenon of Man* (1955), he wrote that humans are evolving toward an ultimate spiritual unity, and he predicted that a global layer of consciousness (a *noosphere*) would supersede the Earth's biosphere.

Bertalanffy classified the evolutionary views of Bergson, Smuts, and Teilhard as vitalistic and therefore of no seminal value to science. He instead drew inspiration about evolution from German poet-philosopher-scientist Johann Wolfgang von Goethe (1749–1832). Though Goethe apparently had no understanding of evolutionary descent—he lived in an age when he and others took it for granted that fleas arose spontaneously from wood shavings and urine—he founded and named the science of *morphology*, which became a major discipline of modern evolutionists. Goethe studied biological forms because of his passionate belief in a universal design of nature; he delighted in collecting evidence of what is now called *homology* (the structural similarity of biological forms, as in the identical design of bones, muscles, blood vessels, and nerves in the forelimbs of humans, dogs, birds, and whales). In Goethe's *Metamorphosis of Plants* (1790), he offered evidence that all existing plants could be traced to a common archetype, which he called an *Urpflanz* (arch-plant). According to Bertalanffy, Goethe "intuitively conceived" general systems theory by postulating "a unity of design within groups of organisms" and thus "a universal law of harmony." Bertalanffy also saw hints of the dynamic aspects of general systems philosophy in Goethe's view that nature's archetypes are not static ideals like those of Plato but are "never-ending streams of becoming" in accordance with the "all is flux" philosophy of Heraclitus.

Another major influence on Bertalanffy's evolutionary thought was Germany's first major Darwinian biologist, Ernst Heinrich Haeckel (1834–1919). Haeckel, a medically trained zoologist, coined the term *ecology* and the concept *ontogeny recapitulates phylogeny* (his Biogenetic Law: embryonic development reenacts evolutionary history). But Haeckel's most memorable contribution, for Bertalanffy, was Haeckel's adoption of the Goethean vision of all nature as a unity, orchestrated by universal natural laws.

Bertalanffy advocated a search for organismic-systems laws of evolution at a number of scientific meetings and in various scientific journals. There is no way of measuring the long-term, rippling effect of his advocacy, but the fact is that a search such as Bertalanffy envisioned is currently underway on the frontiers of evolutionary science. One such effort, involving a widely debated new concept of evolution called *autopoiesis* (self-creation), was introduced into GST literature in the 1970s. A leading exponent, Fordham University operations research specialist Milan Zeleny, describes autopoiesis as a concept that belongs to a new group of theories "addressing the issues of self-organization and spontaneous phenomena within physical, biological, and social systems." The concept suggests that random events such as mutations cause a restructuring of morphogenetic fields (structure-causing forces roughly analogous to gravity fields), which in turn cause an increased probablity of related events. Autopoiesis has been enthusiastically advanced as the hypothesis of *formative causation* by British plant phys-iologist Rupert Sheldrake in a controversial new book called *A New Science of Life*. Another post-Bertalanffy challenge to neo-Darwinian orthodoxy has been introduced by a pair of American paleobiologists, Stephen Jay Gould and Niles Eldridge. In an obscure paper of 1972 and a now-famous paper of 1977, they propounded the idea that Darwinian gradualism is the *exception* to the rule in evolution. The prevailing pattern, in their view, is *punctuated equilibrium*, a series of relatively quick jumps that somehow produce new species without transitional stages. Most missing links are missing, they say, because the links were never there. The important "missing link," as far as they are concerned, is the answer to the question of what causes the quick jumps. Such evolutionary revisionism, according to author Francis Hitching's *The Neck of the Giraffe: Where Darwin Went Wrong* (1982), has produced "a new biology" based on the view that biological forms arose from organismic law rather than random mutations.

If our appearance on this planet has been determined by organismic laws, as Bertalanffy's evolutionary viewpoint suggested, does that mean our individual fate has likewise been determined? Did Bertalanffy reject the mechanism of pure chance only to embrace a mechanism of pure control? Are we nothing but mechanical dancing dolls atop a Lapla-cean music box? No, Bertalanffy responded emphatically when his students raised such questions. He argued: Con-trary to the doctrine of Laplace, the predictability involved in natural law does not apply to individual events. We can predict the collective behavior of trillions of gas molecules in a jar and millions of motorists on the highways, but we cannot predict the collision of individual molecules or motorcars. Moreover, individual unpredictability increases with complexity in nature's hierarchical order of systems. Humans, as the most complex of all living systems, have emerged with the most individual freedom.

Bertalanffy further reconciled free will with natural law by comparing our individual autonomy to that of an artist, whose creative potential actually increases with his increasing knowledge of the nature of the particular artistic medium. In support of Bertalanffy's viewpoint on this question, Koestler likened free will to the liberty of a composer, who is limited by the rules of harmony and the structure of the diatonic scales but who nevertheless is free to compose any number of original creations.

A scientist deeply influenced by an early encounter with Bertalanffy's writing in biology, Anglo-American evolutionary biologist Charles E. Oxnard, has spent the past quarter-century collecting and publishing evidence that *Homo sapiens* has evolved on a unique path of anatomical and mental emergence that fundamentally separates us from the apes. Oxnard tells me: "I believe humans have developed uniquely because of a new series of behavioral-evolutionary changes that have been superimposed on biological-genetic evolution." Oxnard says this new level of evolution has largely freed our species from biological determinism. For better or worse, according to Oxnard (and Bertalanffy before him), our future is in our hands.

In Bertalanffy's worldview, we have no justification for sitting back as if we were letting nature take its course. We are not merely onlookers in nature's game. We are participants. But, because life is governed by the natural laws of systems, a successful participant must learn the rules.

Bertalanffy's emphasis on the evolutionary emergence of human free will placed him in direct opposition to *Social Darwinism* (the philosophy of biological determinism that should have been called Social Spencerianism because it drew on the dog-eat-dog viewpoint of Herbert Spencer, the pre-Darwinian evolutionary philosopher who coined the expression *survival of the fittest*). Bertalanffy, like Darwin, rejected the assumption that human society is biologically ruled by the law of the jungle. Bertalanffy, echoing Darwin's *Descent of Man*, described *Homo sapiens* as a socially-oriented species whose survival has depended at least in part on the development of behavior that is characterized by compassion. Of course, Bertalanffy had no illusions about the human capacity for cruelty. But he was convinced that the human being was the first product of evolution with the ability to choose its behavior. In Bertalanffy's view, humanity's fulfillment depends on our becoming aware of the rules of life so that we can live our lives to the utmost.

GST Roots

As a champion of the search for organismic-systems laws, Bertalanffy did not lay claim to originality. Though he was the first to spell out the organismic-systems conception scientifically and to develop it into a general systems viewpoint, he repeatedly made reference to the fact that concepts for systems in general had been introduced independently by others.

He took pains to point out, for example, that a systems approach to philosophy had been presented in 1912 by the German philosopher Nicolai Hartmann (1882–1950). And, in 1925, in a metaphysical organismic development parallel to Bertalanffy's thought, English philosopher-mathematician Alfred North Whitehead (1861–1947) published *Science and the Modern World*, a book of lectures introducing a God-centered metaphysics based on a non-materialistic universe of "events" that manifest themselves in organisms of living things and also organisms in the form of atoms. In Whitehead's words: "Biology is the study of larger organisms, whereas physics is the study of smaller organisms."

Because of Whitehead's fame, Bertalanffy frequently felt obliged to state that he had been unaware of Whitehead's organismic ideas during the writing of *Modern Theories of Development*. Actually, Bertalanffy's organismic biology was much closer to the thinking of Johns Hopkins University mathematical-biology pioneer Alfred James Lotka (1880–

1949), whose *Elements of Physical Biology* (1925) proposed the search for systems laws on the level of biological populations, and to the thinking of English biologist Edward Stuart Russell (1887–1954), whose *The Interpretation of Development and Heredity* (1930) urged an *organismal*-systems approach to the study of individual organisms. Bertalanffy often cited Lotka as a harbinger of GST. And Bertalanffy remarked about the "striking parallelism" between his own 1928 opus on organismic biology and Russell's 1930 book on organis*mal* biology, concluding that "this correspondence is a sign that this way of thinking is 'in the air' and is forcing itself upon the attention of independent authors."

In another instance of parallelism, the English biologist Joseph Henry Woodger developed an organismic approach to biology, then happened to read Bertalanffy's book in the original German and consequently incorporated some Bertalanffian ideas in his (Woodger's) 1929 book, *Biological Principles*. When Woodger introduced Bertalanffy's thought directly to the English-speaking world by translating the Bertalanffy book, Edward Stuart Russell hailed Bertalanffy as "one of a small band of people who are paving the way to a new conception of the organism."

The organismic-systems viewpoint, usually without explicit reference to Bertalanffy, was adopted (more or less) by such prominent twentieth-century figures as Austrian physicist Erwin Schrödinger, Hungarian-British chemist-philosopher Michael Polanyi, British biologists Joseph Needham and J.B.S. Haldane, and American biologists René Dubos, Theodosius Dobzhansky, Barry Commoner, and Edmund Ware Sinnott. Biologist Sinnott, who did cite Bertalanffy's contribution to organicism, stated in his *Cell and Psyche* (1950) that an understanding of the biological laws of organization would "determine the future of biology and psychology and the whole of man."

Despite the prominence of some organismic biologists, the biology establishment has remained steadfastly mechanistic. A leading biochemist recently confided to me:

We haven't yet followed Bertalanffy's lead because biological research grants and other rewards are all oriented toward the mechanistic approach. So the scientific world still doesn't know what makes an organism organized. That question would be very difficult to research, but I suspect the results would be tremendously valuable to science in general and medicine in particular.

That view was seconded for me by a university biologist whose research on biological processes is funded by the National Science Foundation: "The organizing force of life is not something I think about when I'm working in my laboratory. Scientists like me are paid to think mechanistically, so we do."

A GST-oriented theoretical biologist who was a faculty friend of Bertalanffy at SUNY Buffalo, Robert Rosen, informs me that most biologists today are so faithful to mechanistic reductionism that "they don't consider a biological phenomenon real" unless they feel they can reduce it to an explanation from physics. Says Rosen:

Modern biological experimentalists cannot even conceive of approaching biological organization in any terms except reductionist ones. All of the instruments of molecular biology, for example, have been directly adapted from the tools of atomic physics.

Ironically, while most biologists continue to cling to mechanism, the world of physics has undergone an anti-mechanistic revolution. Savoring that irony, Bertalanffy wrote: "Modern physics has destroyed the concept of matter except as a figure of speech. The ultimate components of physical reality are not small bodies any more, but rather dynamic events." That means, said Bertalanffy, biological mechanists have been basing their reductionist assumptions on a mechanistic model of physics that physicists themselves have discarded. A recent observation of this irony was made in *Psychology Today* by Yale biophysicist Harold J. Morowitz: "It is as if the two disciplines were on fast-moving trains going in opposite directions and not noticing what is happening across the tracks."

Bertalanffy began as early as 1927 to refer to biological implications of a revolution in physics that was demolishing the Newtonian model of a mechanistic universe. By that year, Max Planck (1858–1947) had introduced the notion that energy in the atomic realm moves in measured spurts (*quanta*) rather than a continuous flow, Albert Einstein (1879–1955) had repealed the Newtonian premise of absolute time and space and also had unmasked matter as a manifestation of energy, Werner Karl Heisenberg (1901–1976) had displaced the Laplacean concept of absolute predictability with the Heisenberg principle of indeterminancy, and Niels Bohr (1885–1962) had developed his principle of complementarity to justify the exotic but useful idea that an electron can be viewed as either a particle or a wave.

Though Newton's laws still hold for the measurement of our everyday world of time and space, they no longer serve to describe fundamental reality. In the view of quantum pioneer Schrödinger, the revolution in physics showed that it is "better to regard a particle not as a permanent entity but as an instantaneous event." Schrödinger declared that the essence of matter is not material but "shape and organization." By 1930, mathematician-astronomer Sir James Jeans (1877–1946) was observing that modern physics had made the universe "look more like a great thought than like a great machine."

Today, physics depicts the universe as an expression of energy and organization. As physicist Fritjof Capra observed in his 1982 testimonial for the holistic worldview, *The Turning Point*, "the 'New Physics' is very close to general systems theory."

As Bertalanffy perceived more than half a century ago, theoretical physics has played a fascinating practical joke on the mechanists who dominate biology. Biology's mechanists devoutly believe they can reduce biology to physics. Consequently, when they get around to updating their reductionism, they'll be obliged to find a biological viewpoint that's nonmechanistic. When that happens, the organismic-systems legacy of biologist Ludwig von Bertalanffy will be waiting.

"The concept of 'system,'" Bertalanffy wrote in his last scientific paper, "constitutes a new *paradigm*, to use Thomas Kuhn's expression in his brilliant book, *The Structure of Scientific Revolutions* [1962]." Historian Kuhn, who was responsible for equating the idea of a paradigm-shift with scientific revolution, used the word *paradigm* to mean not just a hypothesis or belief but a whole set of shared premises and values that determines the nature of scientific inquiry. In the Kuhnian sense, the paradigm of a given society is supremely influential because it determines what questions scientists in that society are prompted to ask.

In one of Bertalanffy's last classroom lectures, he said:

> There is this hope—I cannot promise you whether or when it will be realized—that the mechanistic paradigm, with all its implications in science as well as in society and our own private life, will be replaced by an organismic or systems paradigm that will offer new pathways for our presently schizophrenic and self-destructive civilization.

The remainder of this book is devoted to the conceptual map that Bertalanffy prepared for those of us who believe that those new pathways must be found.

4

Bertalanffy Versus Behaviorism:
A WARNING ABOUT DEHUMANIZATION

Bertalanffy warns us that our time as effective human beings and behavioral scientists is limited, as is the time of the world as an effectively human ecology, unless we seriously and creatively face the [fact] that the theory of all the behavioral sciences has been and continues to be mechanistic, and therefore capable only of producing more efficient robots.

Psychiatrist William Gray, chief
editor of *General Systems Theory and Psychiatry*

Having cultivated his general systems theory in biology, Bertalanffy transplanted it to the neighboring field of behavioral science, where he again assumed the role of revolutionary.

He thus developed *organismic-systems psychology*, the application of organismic-systems biology to questions of human behavior. As before, he offered his organismic-systems approach as an alternative to the viewpoint of mechanism. And, as before, his critique was as important as his advocacy. Consequently, this chapter will detail what he opposed before we examine what he proposed.

Bertalanffy introduced his organismic-systems psychology

as the basis for what he called "a new image of man," embodying individual responsibility and individual worth. He called the image *new* to contrast it with the contemporary viewpoints that he identified as *robotomorphism* and *zoomorphism*—of *Homo sapiens* as a conditioned-response robot and as an incorrigible naked ape. Those images were two sides of the same coin of mechanism, as far as Bertalanffy was concerned, inasmuch as mechanists regard apes and all other living organisms as merely complex machines.

"The image of man is not only a theoretical question," Bertalanffy wrote, "it is a question of the preservation of man as human." He believed humanity faces a clear and present danger of being dehumanized, even destroyed, by debasing self-images. He feared that a self-image portraying the human being as just another animal would tend to make us indifferent to social inequities and to make us fatalistic about the recurrence of war. And he feared that an image depicting the human being as merely a physico-chemical machine would tend to justify Big Brother techniques of behavior control. In general, he was concerned that the mechanistic image of man would encourage people in all walks of life to treat their fellow human being as an assembly-line object to be manipulated rather than as a unique individual to be treated with respect.

Bertalanffy began writing and lecturing about his new image of humanity in post-World War Two Vienna. He introduced his new-image viewpoint in America during the 1950s, as a founding fellow at the Center for Advanced Study in the Behavioral Sciences at Stanford, as co-director (with psychiatrist Franz Alexander) of a Psychosomatic Research Institute at Mt. Sinai Hospital in Los Angeles, as a lecturer to psychiatric residents at the University of Southern California, and as a visiting professor at the Menninger Foundation in Topeka. His most extensive new-image statement, in 1966, consisted of a pair of talks at the Heinz Werner Institute of Developmental Psychology, located at Clark University in Worcester, Massachusetts. (That presentation, as noted earlier, was published by the university as a book entitled *Organismic Psychology and Systems Theory* and by Bertalanffy in an expanded version called *Robots, Men and Minds*.)

Meanwhile, Bertalanffy's writings in the yearbooks of the Society for General Systems Research won him further converts in psychiatry, including a pair of forensic psychiatrists in Massachusetts, William Gray and Nicholas D. Rizzo. Beginning in 1965, Gray organized GST sessions at the annual meetings of the American Psychiatric Association. Subsequently, Gray, Rizzo, and psychiatrist Frederick J. Duhl produced a book-length symposium on GST and psychiatry.

In 1967, in recognition of Bertalanffy's contribution to behavioral science, the American Psychiatric Association elected him to the position of honorary fellow. As a maverick in his original discipline who had challenged the establishment in an adjoining area, he was extremely proud of the psychiatric association honor, and he came to regard his new image of humanity as an essential item on the GST agenda.

About seven months before his death, on November 2, 1971, he was honored again by the psychiatric profession as the designee of the first Roy R. Grinker, Sr., lectureship at the Institute for Psychosomatic and Psychiatric Research and Training of the Michael Reese Hospital and Medical Center in Chicago. He devoted that lecture to his "new image" advocacy:

> What is badly needed is a timely image of man. Since the previous proud image derived from religion and philosophy does not serve modern needs efficiently, a new image should be synthesized. . . . I would contend that this is a very important business indeed—to find out what actually is human.

Bertalanffy developed his new image largely to combat what he regarded as a basic fallacy shared by robotomorphism and zoomorphism: the assumption that human behavior is essentially reactive. He called that fallacy the *princi-*

ple of reactivity, according to which all behavior is strictly utilitarian, consisting of the gratification of needs or relaxation of tensions. He identified the chief purveyor of that *homeostasis model of human behavior* as a fellow alumnus of the University of Vienna, Sigmund Freud (1856–1939). Though Bertalanffy lauded Freud's psychoanalytic exploration of the *unconscious*—the concept of an unconscious certainly sounds unmechanistic—Bertalanffy faulted Freud for "reducing human behavior to animal 'drives,' 'instincts,' or [biological] 'tissue needs'—essentially sex, hunger, and aggression." Bertalanffy added: "If [this] principle of homeostatic maintenance is taken as a rule of behavior, the so-called well-adjusted individual will be [defined as] a well-oiled robot."

Bertalanffy also rejected Freud's pronouncement that humans have an animal-inherited instinct for aggression. When that notion was revived during the 1960s by best-sellers that branded *Homo sapiens* as a descendant of killer apes—playwright Robert Ardrey's *African Genesis* (1961) and *The Territorial Imperative* (1966), and zoologist Desmond Morris's *The Naked Ape* (1967)—Bertalanffy was among many scientists who denounced the killer-ape thesis as a mass-merchandised myth. Bertalanffy wrote:

> The theory of man as a mere animal or Naked Ape founders on the elementary fact that humans have culture—articulate language, magic and philosophy, machines and science, swords and atom bombs, cathedrals and department stores and what-not—and that animals, apes included, have nothing of the sort. It is well that we recognize how delicate is the distinction separating man and beast; but just because of this we must not help to destroy it.

Origins of Robotomorphism

Bertalanffy believed that robotic images of humanity had to be rooted out at their source, and he identified the principal source as *behaviorism,* the school of psychology that assumes all organisms, including humans, behave according to strictly mechanistic principles.

When Bertalanffy lectured to his students about behaviorism, he traced it back to the Russian laboratory of medical physiologist Ivan Petrovich Pavlov (1849–1936), who became world-famous as the scientist who conditioned dogs to a bell-food association so that they began salivating when the bell rang without food. Pavlov studied such conditioned reflexes for more than three decades, eventually developing a theory that differences in *human* personality are the result of the varying ways that individuals respond to unpleasant stimuli.

Pavlov, as Bertalanffy pointed out, became a prime inspiration for the founder of behaviorism, Johns Hopkins University psychologist John Broadus Watson (1878–1958). Though Watson's behavioral-science experience was limited to his conditioned-reflex experiments with rats, birds, and monkeys, he introduced an approach to human behavior that was to dominate academic psychology in the United States, and subsequently Europe, for decades. In his seminal scientific paper of 1913, *Psychology as the Behaviorist Views It,* he announced that psychologists should discard all subjective concepts about human behavior—including mind, emotion, and desire—and concentrate exclusively on quantifiable behavior such as conditioned reflexes. The goal of this new orientation, declared Watson, was to develop a science of *behavior control.* As Bertalanffy pointedly noted in his classroom lectures, Watson spent the last period of his working life (1921–46) as an executive in the business of advertising.

Watson's best-known disciple, Harvard experimental psychologist B. F. (Burrhus Frederic) Skinner (1904–), became Bertalanffy's principal behaviorist target. Skinner extended Pavlov's stimulus-response conditioning techniques to what Skinner termed *operant conditioning,* in which the laboratory animal is conditioned to respond to stimuli so that the animal operates on the environment. In a typical example, a rat in a "Skinner box" randomly presses a lever that produces the unexpected reward of a food pellet, and the creature gradually becomes conditioned to press the lever in order to obtain food. In a more complex and celebrated example, Skinner trained pigeons to perform a series of motions that made them appear to be playing ping pong. Like other behaviorists, Skinner advanced the idea that all organisms including humans are stimulus-response machines, to be controlled when necessary by means of operant conditioning.

Skinner's advocacy of behavior control for *Homo sapiens* was spelled out in his 1949 "utopian" novel, *Walden Two*, about a commune whose members have been conditioned to be socially obedient and contented, and in his 1971 behaviorist manifesto, *Beyond Freedom and Dignity*, in which Skinner argued that there is no need for us to fear a behavior-control society because the idea of human freedom is strictly an illusion. Skinner's message in the latter book: inasmuch as humans and rats exist on the same level of behavioral determinism, and inasmuch as humans have been behaving rather foolishly, humanity's leaders should support the advancement of "a science of behavior" that would be employed to "design a culture" in which our species would be trained to cooperate *automatically* with leaders of the future. (Presumably, the populace would cooperate with the same no-nonsense consistency as the rat in a Skinner box.) Anticipating accusations that he was prescribing the ultimate tyranny, Skinner wrote: "The problem is to design a world which will be liked not by people as they are now but by those who will live in it."

Skinner and his fellow behaviorists were vehemently and frequently denounced by Bertalanffy as purveyors of an insidiously misleading half-truth. Bertalanffy conceded that animals could be conditioned to behave like robots and that humans could be conditioned to behave like robotic animals. But he firmly believed that animals are more than machines and that humans are more than animals, and therefore behaviorism is a pseudoscientific license for social manipulation:

If you manipulate a dog according to Pavlov or a rat according to Skinner, you will obtain the results described by those authors. That is, you select [from the animals'] behavioral repertoire such responses as may be controlled by punishment or reward. You *make* the animals into stimulus-response machines or robots [through the process Bertalanffy called progressive mechanization]. The same, of course, is true of humans. Modern psychology has the tricks to turn human beings into subhuman automata.

Skinner, like other behaviorists, insisted that his motives were humanitarian, that operant conditioning could work with positive reinforcement and did not require tactics of punishment, and that operant conditioning held great promise for beneficial behavior-modification in the classroom, in the workplace, in psychotherapy, and in institutions for the psychotic and retarded.

A New Tool for Tyranny

Bertalanffy doubted the long-range value of operant conditioning for such purposes. Moreover, he feared that the behaviorists' declarations of idealism would be of no value for preventing the use of operant conditioning by totalitarian leaders who choose to regard all dissenters as psychotic or retarded and all other people as sheep:

> It appears to matter little whether this totalitarianism is essentially benevolent, as in Huxley's *Brave New World*, or malevolent, as in Orwell's *1984;* or whether [behaviorist techniques] are employed democratically to promote a washing machine or a politician, or autocratically to ensure the reign of a dictator. For it is more than probable that methods used for inconsequential advertising can and will be

employed for the deification of the state, the nation, its leader, or for global war, as those in charge desire. The enormous threat contained in Skinner's latest book is that his is not a program or project to *undo* freedom and dignity but a description of what is [already] widely *realized* in the thought control exerted by the mass media, commercial society, and politics.

Bertalanffy blamed behaviorism not only for supplying the tools for totalitarian behavior-control but also for supplying the pseudoscientific justification. He asserted that amoral mass persuasion tactics are the practical application of a theoretical view that sees in human nature only a slight variation of animal behavior:

> What has been lost—because it was never included in the behaviorists' original premises—are the specifically human features of responsibility, free decision, and true human values. Referring to an expression of the sociologist [David] Riesman [from his 1950 classic, *The Lonely Crowd*], human behavior is increasingly 'other-directed' by the modern methods of mass persuasion and the mass media. External stimuli, continuously repeated and applied in cunning techniques, [are designed to] turn man into a machine.

In the realm of amoral mass persuasion, Bertalanffy singled out for censure a 1934 Ph.D. in psychology from the University of Vienna, Ernest Dichter. Dr. Dichter had begun his career as a Vienna psychoanalyst, then moved to the U.S. and the advertising business in the 1940s. He subsequently organized his own advertising-consultant team of psychologists, sociologists, and anthropologists—the Institute of Motivational Research—at a thirty-room, mountaintop mansion overlooking the Hudson River in upstate New York. Dichter, the dean of motivational research and a self-described behavioral engineer, sold advice to corporations on how, in his words, "to manipulate human motivations and desires." Bertalanffy had no doubt that Dichter served his clients well:

> The motivation research founded by Dr. Dichter is developing into a science of mass persuasion [that] can make the human animal buy everything and anything, from detergents to cigarettes, from cars to American presidents, up to wars and atomic self-destruction. . . . I do not worry that the masses prefer television to Telemann, and boxing to Bach. So they always did and presumably always will. But when the intellectual elite, the thinkers and leaders, see in man nothing but an overgrown rat, and manipulate him accordingly, then it is time to be alarmed.

Had Bertalanffy become an alarmist? If so, he was in the company of no less a worrier than the former director of the Manhattan Project, atomic physicist J. Robert Oppenheimer (1904–1967), who in 1955 told the American Psychological Association that the physicist's power to control nuclear reactions was "trivial" compared with the psychologist's emerging power to control human behavior.

As might be expected, Bertalanffy was an avid reader of author-journalist Vance Packard's *The Hidden Persuaders* (1957), the first in-depth study of motivational research. The book, which sold more than three million copies in twelve languages, detailed the work of Dichter and his Madison Avenue disciples; and it examined the latest motivational research technology, including (the questionably effective but nevertheless questionably ethical) subliminal communication in the form of radio, television, and film messages transmitted beneath the receiver's level of conscious awareness and judgment. Packard concluded his book with a warning that "the moral implications of such mass persuasion techniques need to be faced." Looking backward, it appears that none of Packard's readers responded to that challenge with more profound concern than Bertalanffy.

Bertalanffy was aware, as a scholar of history, that mass persuasion was nothing new. But his knowledge of both history and behavioral science led him to conclude that the problem had taken on a frighteningly new form. He noted that, in the past, up to and including the time of Hitler, mass persuasion had been generally practiced as a craft. But now it had become a science, employing psychological techniques that replace old-fashioned external pressure with modern internal conditioning.

Explaining the new power of "internal" persuasion as compared with conventional "external" persuasion, Bertalanffy told a class at SUNY Buffalo:

> You know, dictators in previous times had to apply rather nasty punishment and concentration camps and such. But today we have conditioning by way of gratification, with positive reinforcement, so that the persuader's motives become your motives and thus the persuader has much more power over you than if he had used punishment. This is the way of modern behavioral engineering.

Bertalanffy became convinced that modern behavioral modification technology ultimately could result in a psychological genocide that he and like-minded writers called *menticide:*

> In the end, the effects of modern behavioral engineering amount to functional decerebralization— that is to say, exclusion of higher cerebral centers and mental faculties almost as efficiently as if these were removed by surgical operation. . . . [Such] menticide is highly successful and [potentially] irreversible. If a population is manipulated in the right ways, it cannot transmit, to coming generations, values and freedom it has lost itself.

His position on this issue delineated a crucial difference

between his GST psychology and the psychology of behaviorism. Whereas Bertalanffy *dreaded* the possibility that
a behavior-modified population would never want to rebel,
Skinner viewed that prospect as positively *utopian*. While
Skinner saw modern mass-persuasion as a potential tool
for leaders with far-sighted wisdom, Bertalanffy saw it as
a potential form of power for leaders with blind ambition.

Bertalanffy's concern about the mass-merchandising of
political leaders was reinforced by journalist Joe McGinniss'
1969 bestseller about the first successful Nixon campaign
for the White House, *The Selling of the President 1968*. By
way of introducing almost 300 pages of behind-the-scenes,
anecdotal evidence that candidate Nixon had been merchan-
dised to the public by professional mass persuaders, McGin-
nis wrote: "It is not surprising . . . that politicians and advertising men could have discovered one another . . . once
they recognized that the citizen did not so much vote for
a candidate as make a psychological purchase of him." Bertalanffy enthusiastically recommended the book to his students, jokingly and unknowingly anticipating Watergate by
asking the students not to turn him in to the FBI.

Dissenting from Dissent

During the 1960s, of course, dissent had become fashionable on university campuses. However, Bertalanffy's intellectual independence obliged him to dissent even from the
dissenters. He favored sweeping social reform, but he felt
that those who celebrate the emergence of an imaginary
reform movement are diverting attention from the need to
work for the real thing. Consequently, while warning
against mechanistic-commercial forces that seemed bent on
turning *Homo sapiens* into a zoomorphic/robotomorphic *bête
machine*, Bertalanffy also warned against what he perceived
as a flight toward false alternatives: commercialized versions
of a "counterculture" and a "humanistic psychology."

"It is ironic," he wrote in *The Philosophy Forum* of June

1971, "that efforts to overcome the 'robot man' of commercial society have themselves become objects of commercialism. Growth centers, rock festivals, astrology, and a whole industry catering to dissatisfied youth have themselves become profiteers of the society they condemn." In a psychiatry journal early the following year, he gave his opinion of the two bibles of the counterculture, San Francisco State University historian Theodore Roszak's *The Making of a Counter Culture* (1969) and Yale Law Professor Charles A. Reich's introduction to a so-called new level of consciousness, *The Greening of America* (1971):

> [Their] criticism of corporate society and the psychological wasteland of our times was appropriate enough. The remedies proposed: drugs, rock music, beards, bell-bottom trousers, commune living, and exotic religions—and this is the rather complete list of what the "counterculture" has to offer for saving humanity—were juvenile and silly.

With the counterculture mirage already beginning to fade at the start of the 1970s, Bertalanffy devoted more critical attention to the growing appeal of what he referred to as "so-called humanistic psychology." He believed this movement was especially seductive because it had started with valid premises and authentic intellectual leadership. He lauded humanistic psychologist Abraham Maslow (1908–1970) for going beyond behaviorism and psychoanalysis to depict the human personality as a self-actualizing entity with a basic need for creative expression. Bertalanffy similarly admired, and was admired by, humanistic psychologist Gordon W. Allport (1887–1967), who taught that each human personality is a complex and unique system with the ability to transcend its hereditary and infantile legacies. Bertalanffy also praised the humanistic approach to developmental psychology in the work of Switzerland's Jean Piaget (1896–1980) and German-American psychologist Heinz Werner (1890–1964). Unfortunately, Bertalanffy maintained, humanistic psychology had been largely co-opted by hucksters:

Encounter groups, T-groups [training groups] and the "human potential movement" became an industry run by practitioners with highly questionable credentials. While in part using respectable techniques of group therapy, humanistic psychology became big business—with sensitivity training, nude marathons, and the like, offering a shortcut to an emotional high with sometimes devastating results.

Meanwhile, he contended, the unorthodox fashions in psychotherapy were actually perpetuating the orthodox behaviorist model of humankind: as objects or creatures to be manipulated. For Bertalanffy, the environment of commercialized encounter groups was depressingly similar to the environment of Skinner boxes. The alternative, said Bertalanffy, was a real revolution in psychology: a GST approach to human behavior, based on "a new image of man."

A Continuing Concern

Have Bertalanffy's concerns about dehumanization remained relevant? Consider the following:

1972:   In *The Will to be Human*, psychiatrist Silvano Arieti warns that the behaviorists' mechanistic view of our species could become a self-fulfilling prophecy.

1973:   In *Subliminal Seduction*, communications expert Wilson Bryan Key charges that every major advertising agency has at least one "subliminal technician," injecting subliminal cues in audio and video fare and in printed matter.

1975:   A sequel to the "Naked Ape" controversy begins with publication of a book whose title, *Sociobiology*, introduces a discipline to study "the biological basis of all forms of social behavior in all kinds of organisms, including humans." The author, Harvard zoologist Edward Osborne Wilson, an authority on social insects, announces that "the biological principles which now appear to be working reasonably well for animals in general can be extended profitably to the social sciences."

1977: Vance Packard's *The People Shapers* exposes "new technologists who draw primarily upon discoveries in the behavioral, biological, and computer sciences and who work for institutions, including governments, to help those institutions increase their power to control us and to impose their values and views on others."

1978: In *The Psychological Society,* author-journalist Martin L. Gross indicts the commercialized group-therapy movement for preaching the liberation of self-actualization while practicing the authoritarianism of group conformity.

1981: An Associated Press story, circulated to millions of readers, quotes an animal behaviorist at Central Washington University, psychologist Roger Fouts, as declaring that a belief in human uniqueness is no longer justified now that chimpanzees have been taught to use some elements of human sign language. Nowhere in the story is the reader informed that human uniqueness rests not on the ability to ape language but on our ability to create a whole world of *symbols*—a basic aspect of the Bertalanffian "image of man" to be explored in the next chapter.

5

Systems Psychology:

A NEW IMAGE OF MAN

If there be a third revolution, after the psychoanalytic and behavioristic, it is in development of Bertalanffy's general systems theory.

> Roy R. Grinker, Sr.,
> Chairman Emeritus,
> Department of Psychiatry,
> Michael Reese Hospital and
> Medical Center, Chicago

Bertalanffy's "new image of man" was projected on three levels, each with profound implications:

We are systems.

We are open systems.

We are open systems with uniquely human qualities.

The model of the human being as a system is basic to every Bertalanffian insight about human behavior. This GST principle holds that we must learn to see the individual human being as a whole dynamic entity rather than as an assortment of parts, processes, and traits. For example, if we equate our fellow human with a single characteristic such as gender, age, race, or nationality, or even with an aggregate of such categories, we are perceiving our own labels rather than that person's reality. The result, Bertalanffy advised, is the tendency for us to treat each other as objects, or, at best, as fragments of whole persons.

In that one insight, he targeted the fallacy of prejudice that has poisoned the relations between sexes, generations, races, and nations. If we could see each other as complex systems rather than as embodiments of one or more traits, he suggested, the world might be able to achieve a revolution of harmony. Imagine, he speculated, what might happen to U.S.-Soviet relations if we stopped seeing each other as nothing but capitalists and communists and began seeing each other as complex and ever-changing human beings.

By emphasizing that the human personality is more than the sum of its parts, Bertalanffy acknowledged an agreement with *gestalt psychology*, which had been introduced early in the century in Austria and south Germany by experimental psychologist Max Wertheimer (1880–1943) and his colleagues, Kurt Koffka (1886–1941) and Wolfgang Köhler (1887–1967). Though their original focus was on sensory perception—they demonstrated that we perceive patterns or configurations (*Gestalten*) rather than sums of sensations—they founded a school of psychology that was to call attention to the holistic nature of human behavior in general. The founding Gestaltist or Configurationist, Wertheimer, emphatically rejected the behaviorists' attempts to dissect human behavior into units of response and insisted instead that "the whole [of behavior] determines the nature of its parts."

Bertalanffy's systems view of the human organism had its point of departure in his consideration of the age-old riddle called *the mind-body problem*. The mind-body problem is a cluster of questions. Does mind exist? If it does, what is its nature and how does it relate to the body? If the relationship is strictly parallel and therefore separate, how can we explain the indisputable observation that human ideas repeatedly have changed the face of this planet? If the relationship is one of interaction, how can we explain the phenomenon of a non-material entity acting on a material entity, and vice versa?

No other problem appears to have attracted so much attention from so many philosophers for so many years with so little consensus. The ancient Greek Anaxagoras thought he solved the problem for all time by concluding that mind is the creator and controller of matter. But the question has remained moot for thousands of years. Some of the most prominent arguments were forcefully articulated in the seventeenth century: English materialist Thomas Hobbes declared that the only reality is matter in motion, which creates the illusion of mind; Dutch pantheist Benedict de Spinoza declared that the only reality is a single substance composing God or Nature, of which mind and body are manifestations; German Rationalist Gottfried Wilhelm Leibniz declared that everything we think is a substance is really a *monad* or soul; and the French mechanist Catholic René Descartes proclaimed a mind-body dualism, in which he postulated a subjective reality of mind (*res cogitans*) and an objective reality of matter (*res extensa*).

Bertalanffy considered the basic question of the mind-body problem to be the riddle of mind-body interaction. To consider an everyday example, how do objective electromagnetic waves cause us to experience something as subjective as redness or greenness? That type of experience is so far removed from objective reality that there is absolutely no way it can be described to someone who was born blind. And, having experienced redness or greenness in a situation involving a traffic signal, how do we perform the feat of making our body respond to our mental command to obey the traffic law? Putting the problem in other ways, how does the conscious mind move an arm or leg, while the unconscious mind produces an ulcer? How can the mind feel pain in a limb that has been amputated? How, with yoga and biofeedback, can we will a change in heartbeat or blood pressure? How do mood-altering drugs change the way we feel? How do we experience a cure as a result of our belief in a placebo?

Bertalanffy was among the seminal thinkers of the twentieth century—along with such figures as Scottish zoologist D'Arcy Thompson, psychologist Abraham Maslow, and neurobiologist Roger Sperry—who had the uncommon sense to see the mind-body problem as an illusion. He perceived that many of the great philosophers from ancient Greece onward had been baffling themselves with a riddle of their own making. They had been attempting to reconcile a mind-body antithesis that simply does not exist. Mind and body as separate entities are linguistic fictions, he argued. They are conceptual distortions that have blurred our vision of reality, afflicting us with double vision of a single entity.

Mind-body separateness was presumed to exist, said Bertalanffy, because separate concepts for mind and body were built into our language. He speculated that mind-body dualism was a myth that evolved during a long process of Western civilization's linguistic-cultural development. He thought it might be a myth that reflects the culturally evolved idea of the "self" as an entity that is totally separate from the external world. In contrast, no such dichotomy exists in many non-Western and so-called primitive cultures, where self and cosmos are one or at least a continuum. In our own culture, Bertalanffy observed, similar "mystic" perception can be found among infants, schizophrenics, and persons under the influence of mescaline and LSD.

Convinced as he was that mind-body dualism is a myth, Bertalanffy called for the demolition of the academic walls that separate biology from psychology, just as he had preached and practiced the unity of botany and zoology in a first-of-its-kind integrated biology course he taught at the University of Vienna School of Medicine. In the biology-psychology case, his call for integration went unheeded; today's university programs in psychobiology are generally behavioristic approaches to the biological bases of behavior. A university administrator recently told me: "Bertalanffy was completely right about the idea that biology and psychology are really the same discipline. The only reason they remain in separate departments at universities is that neither side wants to surrender its fiefdom."

If psychology and biology are one, Bertalanffy continued, then so are psychiatry and medicine. Therefore, psychotherapists need to become more attuned to the somatic causes of mental illness, and physicians need to become more alert to the emotional causes of physical illness. He wrote: "A very old and basic philosophic question, the mind-body problem, now becomes a medical and clinical problem: how are the reciprocal actions between somatic disorders and psychic factors to be understood?"

The Human System

In a discussion about Bertalanffy's views on this topic with the father of micro-neurosurgery, Dr. Theodore Kurze of Huntington Memorial Hospital in Pasadena, I was told that ignorance of and carelessness about the psychosomatic facts of life are "about equal among physicians and psychiatrists." As an example from the latter category, he cited a case of a woman who spent many years being psychoanalyzed because of uncontrollable rages, which Kurze discovered had been caused by a brain tumor. On the other side of the psychosomatic fence, I obtained confirming testimony from Los Angeles psychiatrist Warren R. Procci, who had studied Bertalanffy's organismic psychology during training to qualify as a psychoanalyst. Dr. Procci endorses the GST viewpoint that no malady is all in the mind, just as no malady is all in the body: "For example, though doctors tend to regard hypochondria as a nonexistent problem, the victims actually suffer real pain and can 'think' themselves into real pathology."

According to Bertalanffian mind-body unity, can we also think ourselves *out* of real pathology? To be sure, much that passes for psychic healing is quackery in the sense that the "healer" uses the power of suggestion to remove symptoms rather than the disease, thereby jeopardizing life by removing vital warning signals. But a growing number of orthodox healers are investigating the possibility that suggestion may contribute to an actual cure. One of the best-known converts to this position is Dr. Carl Simonton, a

Fort Hood, Texas, radiologist who reports encouraging results from his dozen years of combining conventional cancer therapy with instructions to the patient about the use of mental imagery to encourage the body's immuno-suppressive system by means of "picturing" the body's destruction of the malignant cells. I've seen a Simonton-oriented clinical psychologist give cancer patients this instruction under hypnosis; I've heard patient testimonials of cancer remission; and I've been impressed at least by the fact that this approach is cautiously offered as a supplement rather than as an alternative to conventional treatment.

Long before the phrase *holistic medicine* became popular, and commercially distorted, Bertalanffy urged that the holistic viewpoint be adopted by the medical profession. Having spent many years teaching biology to medical students, he was not shy about prescribing for MDs. Every patient, he urged, should be diagnosed and treated as a "psychophysical whole" rather than as a fever, fracture, or phobia. He took notice of the lip-service eventually paid to holistic medicine, but he observed that truly holistic care was a rare practice in an age of assembly-line treatment, increasing medical specialization, and the near-extinction of the old-fashioned, house-calling family doctor. As the trend toward medical specialization accelerated during his senior years, he decried it as a "dehumanization of medicine," and he characterized the mechanistically inclined medical specialist as "a sort of glorified auto mechanic, setting this or that organ right, transplanting or inserting artificial organs, with the effect that the whole or system, the patient as a human being, is often overlooked." I obtained a similar opinion about this aspect of medical specialization from pharmacist Max Stollman, former president of the California Pharmacists Association: "The family-practice pharmacist today sometimes discovers that patients who see more than one specialist at a time are being given prescriptions that combine in ways that tend to reduce the drugs' effectiveness and in some cases pose a threat to the patient's health because of the phenomenon of *synergism* [the combined effect

is greater than, and hazardously different from, the sum
of the separate effects]."

Bertalanffy's repugnance for fragmented, mechanistic
medicine was reinforced by personal experience a year before his death. As related earlier, he suffered a mild heart
attack, and he was ordered by his physician to spend three
precautionary weeks in a hospital. Not being in particular
discomfort or fear, he devoted most of that time to reading,
writing, and observing. Later, he wove his hospital observations into a talk on general systems theory to a class of
student nurses:

> You find some nice nurses in a hospital. But health
> care has become progressively mechanized and de-
> humanized. No attempt is made to satisfy the human
> need for intimacy, thus losing the old-fashioned
> human touch that can help some patients *will* their
> recovery. Too many hospitals today are like a health
> factory, an assembly line with an "input" of patients
> who are processed and who then become "output."
> The patient becomes diagnostically a bundle of tests,
> a thing rather than a person. And the personal diag-
> nosis is being replaced by computers. One explanation
> for this is bigness. But the more important problem
> is that modern medicine is using a mechanistic ap-
> proach, treating the patient like an injured machine
> rather than applying the humanistic-systems-organis-
> mic approach.

Humans as Open Systems

Far-reaching implications for medical, psychological and
social aspects of the human condition are involved at the
second level of Bertalanffy's new image of humanity: the
individual as an open system.

Like other basic tenets of GST, the model of the human
being as an open system is so obvious that it may easily

be dismissed as trivial. But the same may be said of Newton's legendary falling apple. Everybody knew that apples and other objects fall to the ground. The genius of people like Newton (and Bertalanffy) consists of their ability to convert that which we take for granted into that which we can put to use, and of determining which of many obvious phenomena are worth contemplating.

The first step in the productive contemplation of the obvious, Bertalanffy knew, was to establish a working definition. All open systems, the reader will recall, were defined by Bertalanffy as systems that maintain a steady state by continuously exchanging matter and energy with the environment. *Steady state* was Bertalanffy's term for flow-equilibrium as opposed to stationary equilibrium. To recap further, he held that *steady state* meant that open systems are not just in flux, they *are* flux. Consequently, to borrow from the convenient shorthand of general semantics—a school of thought joined by GST thinker Rapoport and praised by Bertalanffy for some insights that coincided with concepts of GST—not only does Frenchman[1] not equal Frenchman[2] but Frenchman[1] of yesterday does not necessarily equal Frenchman[1] of today.

Though Bertalanffy did not take the time to spell out the human consequences of open-systems flux, he knew that volumes could be written about that subject. Consider, for example, how many parents have alienated themselves from their children by failing to see that the child has grown up, how many marriages have dissolved because one or both partners failed to see that the opposite number had developed new needs and goals, how many businesses have gone bankrupt because the owners failed to see changes in public demand, and how many national leaders have courted disaster because they failed to see that yesterday's policies don't necessarily fit the needs of today's world. In all such cases, the difference between success and failure may be a matter of reminding ourselves that people are open systems and therefore are subject to continuous change, because that is human nature.

Bertalanffy's sensitivity to flux was partly evident in his indefatigable, continuous renewal of his own education. His awareness of flux also could be seen in his role as a lifelong political outsider, who stayed off everybody's bandwagon because none of them, in his view, kept up with the flow of contemporary events. Decades before author Alvin Toffler's *Future Shock* (1970), Bertalanffy began warning that humanity's leaders habitually stumble from one crisis to another because they generally view the world through spectacles of their past.

The most significant characteristic of Bertalanffy's open systems model of the human organism is the basic fact of its being open. As the poet John Donne observed more than three centuries ago: "no man is an iland, intire of itselfe." Consequently, according to Bertalanffy, anyone who wishes to understand an individual human being must take into account that person's continuous interactions with the environment. Bertalanffy's open systems model of the individual overlapped the neo-Gestalt *field theory* of German-American social psychologist Kurt Lewin (1890–1947), who stated: "To understand or predict behavior, the person and his environment have to be considered as one constellation of interdependent factors." In anthropology, Bertalanffy's open systems model was in effect confirmed by Margaret Mead (1901–1978), whose field work showed that sex roles and other aspects of social behavior are determined more by culture than by biology. In all of its behavioral applications, Bertalanffy's open systems concept highlighted the hope that we can reform patterns of human behavior by changing the human environment or by changing our way of interacting with the environment.

In the field of medicine, Bertalanffy noted, Hippocrates (460–377 B.C.) is said to have told his students that the first step in medical care is to assess the patient's air, water, liquor, diet, "sexualities," and "politics." But the open-system implications of that ancient advice have been ignored by the all-too-numerous physicians who view the patient as an isolated unit without due regard to the potential medical influences at the patient's home or workplace. That failure commonly contributes to tragic results among patients who suffer heart attacks, according to what I've been told by a prominent cardiologist who has been quietly campaigning within his field for patient-counseling programs of "psychosocial intervention." A cure for any serious condition may be of little help if the patient is to be continually subject to environmental relapse or perhaps re-infection. Moreover, a cure is not likely to occur at all if medications and medical advice are negated by environmental factors that cause or contribute to noncompliance.

Within the healing arts, the most enthusiastic and numerous admirers of Bertalanffy's open systems model are psychiatrists. Former American Psychiatric Association president Judd Marmor, who was on the staff of Los Angeles' Mt. Sinai Hospital when Bertalanffy served there (1955–58), tells me:

> Bertalanffy's concept of the human being as an open system significantly influenced my thinking and that of many others in psychiatry. In our traditional Freudian approach, we tended to concentrate exclusively on the inner perceptions of the patient. But Bertalanffy showed us the decisive importance of the patient's interaction with the environment—personal, social and occupational. If there's a family problem, we systems psychiatrists try to work with a significant member or members of the family as well as with the original patient. If the patient is a child, we treat the child with the family, and we deal with the home environment in which the child's problem arose. In every case in which we apply the systems approach, we are likely to get results that are better and faster.

Bertalanffy's best-known admirer in psychiatry was Karl Menninger. Dr. Menninger consulted frequently with Bertalanffy during the years 1958–60, when Bertalanffy served as a visiting professor at the Menninger Foundation. Bertalanffy thus contributed to the development of Menninger's holistic *unitary concept,* a view of mental illness as a systems disorder. That concept promised a major reform for twentieth-century psychiatric thought by diverting attention away from traditional psychiatric labels and focusing instead on the systems dynamics that are common to all forms of psychopathology. A confidante of both Menninger and Bertalanffy, psychiatrist Frederick J. Hacker of the Hacker Psychiatric Clinic in Beverly Hills, recalls: "It was Karl's interest in general systems theory that caused him to seek out Ludwig. Karl had had systems ideas of his own for many years, but he had never been able to formulate them clearly until he interacted personally with Ludwig."

Bertalanffy frequently expressed his pride in having contributed to Menninger's unitary concept. In a passage from a posthumous collection of Bertalanffy's papers, *A Systems View of Man,* Bertalanffy stated: "The unitary concept of mental illness, propounding that mental disorder is a systemic disease rather than a number of separate diseases, I believe represents a major breakthrough in psychiatry, which may lead to a basic reorientation in theory and clinical practice."

For Menninger, the admiration was mutual: "I consider Dr. von Bertalanffy to be one of my most influential teachers, one who changed many of my opinions in various respects." In Menninger's principal statement of his unitary concept, *The Vital Balance* (1963), he identified the concept's basic premise as "the steady state of the open system, as defined by von Bertalanffy." And, in the spirit of Bertalanffy's GST, Menninger called for an end to treating mental illness as if it were a thing and the beginning of an approach that would help disturbed individuals restore the "vital balance" among such factors as external relationships, internal relationships, and the adjustment of those factors with the ever-changing effects of time and growth. A formidable task, yes. But Menninger, like Bertalanffy, voiced the opinion that it was better to face real complexities rather than to waste time on the misleading simplicities of psychiatric labels.

In the neighboring field of marriage and family counseling, Bertalanffy's open-systems model has been winning "immense" popularity in recent years, according to marriage scholars Marcia and Thomas Lasswell in their *Marriage and the Family* (1982). They report that they and other members of their profession are finding GST a revealing perspective on the interaction between family members and between the family and its environment. However, such sophistication about marriage apparently has not yet spread to society at large. Half of all recent marriages are heading for divorce, to judge from current statistics. Perhaps that's because society tends to define marital compatibility in terms of the similarity or complementarity of the partners' traits rather than in terms of the nature of the relationship that emerges from the partners' interaction. People who seem perfect *for* each other often turn out to be miserable *with* each other. If the GST viewpoint spreads, we will be less likely to ask, "What does she (he) see in him (her)?" and more likely to ask, "What does she (he) see in their relationship?" This writer suspects that a huge amount of misery could be prevented with such systems-semantic reform.

As noted in a preceding chapter, another trait that Bertalanffy correlated with open systems is equifinality: the system's inner-directed ability to protect or restore wholeness. Because every human being exhibits "equi-final self-preservation," Bertalanffy advocated that modern physicians follow the example of Renaissance Swiss physician-chemist Paracelsus (1493–1541), who pioneered in pharmacology but nevertheless emphasized the body's powers of self-healing. Too often, said Bertalanffy, the body's natural healing powers are thwarted by well-intentioned but harmful medical intervention.

A member of the medical profession who read Bertalanffy and heeded him on this point was endocrinologist F. Eugene Yates, M.D., director of the UCLA Crump Institute for Medical Engineering: "In line with Bertalanffy's insight about equifinality, I've been studying the human body as a self-regulating open system, because I believe medicine someday will make significant progress by learning to work in harmony with the body's natural rhythms and defenses. For example, I've been investigating the body's normal insulin mechanism to determine how we can emulate it more precisely in caring for insulin-dependent diabetics so that we possibly may lessen or eliminate such diabetes-related afflictions as cardiovascular disease and blindness."

The meaning of Bertalanffy's phrase "equi-final self-preservation" was epitomized by something Albert Schweitzer said to Norman Cousins when Cousins asked why jungle witch doctors have such a high rate of cures. Dr. Schweitzer chuckled and responded: "You're asking me to reveal a trade secret all of us doctors have known for centuries. The answer is that every patient carries his own doctor in his head, and a good doctor simply gets the mental doctor going."

Yet another humanly relevant aspect of open systems, said Bertalanffy, is spontaneity. As noted previously, Bertalanffy held that all living organisms, as open systems, are characterized by spontaneous activity rather than mere reactivity to environmental stimuli. Moreover, in animals and particularly in humans, he identified much of this spontaneity as nonutilitarian: having nothing to do with the homeostatic process of satisfying biological-survival needs or the need to release tensions. In support of his position, he often reminded his readers that even homeostasis pioneer Walter Bradford Cannon had stressed that human behavior consists of many "priceless unessentials" *beyond* homeostasis. Bertalanffy wrote:

> In the sense of homeostasis, Michelangelo should have followed his father's advice and gone into the stonecutting business. He would have had a much happier life than the one he led painting [the more than three hundred figures on the ceiling of] the Sistine Chapel in a very uncomfortable position. . . . Just what we consider the specifically human achievements can hardly be brought under the utilitarian maintenance scheme. If, as has been done, you subsume mountain climbing or writing lyrical poems

[both of which Bertalanffy did in his youth] under the notion of homeostasis, the concept becomes a cover-all, devoid of any meaning.

Bertalanffy conceded that many victims of psychopathology withdraw into stimulus-response passivity and/or homeostatic obsessions with food and sex. However, for Bertalanffy, this was only further evidence that spontaneous behavior is normal. A psychiatrist who has emphatically seconded that opinion, GST disciple William Gray, maintains that, because we are open systems in the Bertalanffian sense, our well-being depends on our having adequate outlets for inner-directed, spontaneous urges. Gray writes: "The practice of psychiatry offers abundant evidence of man's favorable response to an approach that centers on his potential for independence, creativeness, spontaneity, and playfulness." Gray consequently recommended that psychotherapists be continuously alert for relevant bursts of spontaneity from neurotically robotic patients, so that those creative impulses can be encouraged. Likewise, Gray found valuable clinical insights in Bertalanffy's view of life as a phenomenon of creative growth:

> Bertalanffy's basic ideas of anamorphosis [the natural tendency toward increasing complexity] and open systems are vital to psychiatry and have rejuvenated its approach. It is surprising to note the degree to which a closed-system model has dominated psychiatric thought, in the form of assumptions that what was inside a person was fixed at birth. The notion of anamorphosis means to psychiatrists that growth and development are a continuing process as long as life lasts, except in the presence of severe psychiatric, social, physical, and cultural pathology.

To ignore spontaneity in organisms, said Bertalanffy, is to ignore the potential of creativity in those organisms we call human. In line with that view, he often expressed concern that the stimulus-response (S-R) model of human behavior had what he regarded as an enormous impact on the theory and practice of education.

He blamed the S-R model for what he perceived as the prevailing tendency of schoolteachers to attempt to pour knowledge into their pupils' heads as if children were empty jars, passively waiting to be filled. He also blamed S-R-oriented teachers for smothering childhood spontaneity and thus fostering future generations of robotic consumers and soulless scientists. In opposition to the S-R doctrine of primary reactivity, and on behalf of the open-systems principle of primary activity and spontaneity, Bertalanffy urged that teachers foster each child's "natural curiosity and creativity, the desire for exploration [and] inherent pleasure in activity and function." Bertalanffy endorsed linguist Noam Chomsky's position that children begin school with an innate intellectual curiosity, a drive to discover and invent, that too often is stifled by poorly trained or inadequately motivated teachers. The child starts out with a hunger for knowledge, in Bertalanffy's view, but the hunger is overwhelmed by scholastic force-feeding. For Bertalanffy, quality education always was and always will be that which is conducted in the "the classical sense of unfolding human potentialities." Education that is purely "utilitarian" is thus ultimately contrary to human purposes. Scientific courses on know-how, he said, should be complemented by humanities courses on know-why:

It is precisely the definition of the cultural values of art, poetry, history, and so forth, that they have no short-range, utilitarian values. They are goals in themselves. But, for exactly that reason, they have a utilitarian value at a higher level. The poor creature called man—beset with the shortcomings of animal physiology, aggravated by domestication, making his living in a continuous rat-race, under a thousand stresses, and chased around in a complex society—transcends the image of an overburdened Pavlovian dog only by those seemingly useless, but so indispensable, realms of his more-than-animal being.

Bertalanffy's concept of primary activity was his principal topic as a 1956 guest of the World Health Organization's Research Study Group on the Psychobiological Development of the Child. The group's members, who included ethologist Konrad Lorenz, anthropologist Margaret Mead, and developmental biologist Jean Piaget, invited Bertalanffy to attend their fourth and final annual meeting in Geneva. As reported in the official record: "In its search for a synthesis, the group was aided by a presentation on general systems theory from a new guest, Professor Ludwig von Bertalanffy." Piaget's opening paper for this meeting suggested that a synthesis of multidisciplinary approaches to questions of human development would necessitate a search for an interdisciplinary language. Bertalanffy recommended the language of GST. After outlining the GST premises, Bertalanffy suggested that his term *steady state* be used in place of Piaget's *equilibrium factor*, which referred to the child's drive for a state of balance. Bertalanffy explained that his term incorporated the idea that the individual is a dynamic, inner-directed open system rather than a mechanistic model of homeostasis. Piaget agreed with Bertalanffy's psychological viewpoint but he dismissed the semantic advice: "If I understood Bertalanffy properly, he defined 'steady state' exactly in the sense in which I speak of equilibrium." In retrospect, it appears unfortunate that Piaget dismissed Bertalanffy's counsel: a *Science 81* magazine review of an English translation of Piaget's *Experiments in Contradiction* (1974) complains of Piaget's "typical, jargon-ridden prose" after citing the example of Piaget's explanation of a child's primary motivation for learning as a drive toward *equilibrium*. As Bertalanffy had foreseen, Piaget's terminology had concealed Piaget's wisdom.

Bertalanffy was nothing short of passionate about the importance of nurturing individual creativity, and he was vehemently opposed to any influence that seemed to place it in jeopardy. For example, in his immediate world of academic science, he often denounced what he perceived as a widespread and stultifying "mystical belief" in the group, team, or committee. He recognized that teamwork can be productive and even indispensable in the application of ideas, but not in their origination. He rejected the belief that group brainstorming could produce new basic discoveries. Most scientific breakthroughs, he contended, were achieved by gifted individuals, often by nonconformists who were regarded as prima donnas. In defense of such persons, Bertalanffy wrote:"You cannot hear opera without prima donnas, and you cannot promote science without leaders." His belief in the importance of the creative individual took precedence even over his allegiance to holism: "The expectation that a scientific team is more creative than the sum of its members rests on the metaphysical [and unfounded] belief that a social group has a 'mind' or 'spirit' excelling that of the component individuals." Though that may sound like a contradiction of his general systems theory, it actually was a confirmation that he was the father of what in his later years became known as *humanistic general systems theory*. Bertalanffian GST *is* humanistic GST, which means that the body of his thought cannot be fully appreciated without that adjective. For Bertalanffy, the system we call the human individual holds a uniquely important rank among all other systems.

A Parody of Democracy

Only within this context of Bertalanffian individualism is it possible to understand his opposition to what he considered a distortion of democracy in the field of education. During the 1960s and early 1970s, when rights for minorities and women entered the mainstream of the American consciousness, Bertalanffy wrote and lectured against what he called the dogma of *egalitarianism.* Identifying egalitarianism as the "perspective [that] insists that all individuals have equal capabilities and intelligence," he called it "a parody of the American Constitution." He wrote:

> The Founding Fathers certainly did not envisage or aspire to the manufacture of mass men in commercialized society. The consequence of [egalitarian] theory, however, is the orientation of education to fit the lowest common denominator, that is, the lowest intelligence level in the group. The results are that Johnny can't read, that he compares unfavorably with little Ivan, and that college students cannot speak or write decent English.

While supporting egalitarianism in the idealistic sense of equal opportunity, he opposed educational and other policies that translated equal opportunity into equal rewards that are bestowed regardless of individual accomplishments and abilities. His purpose was to defend individual incentive and creativity. But some of his friends felt called upon to "forgive" him for being an "elitist." One of these friends, a well-known psychoanalyst, recently confided: "Ludwig had so much to offer on so many other intellectual levels that I chose never to jeopardize our friendship by arguing with him on this point." It's a shame that the discussion never took place, because Bertalanffy would have been able to offer a thought-provoking explanation, as he did one spring day in 1971 to a systems philosophy class:

> When I attack this principle of doctrinaire egalitarianism, please don't think I am taking a standpoint of elitism or racism or the Social Darwinism that preaches Nazi-like survival of the strongest. If I stress the scientific fact that individuals and groups exhibit differences, that does not mean I look at those differences in terms of superiority or inferiority. I simply do not want individual potential to be crushed by

the egalitarian steamroller, as it were, which tends to level everyone to the lowest common denominator. . . . As a biologist, I can say that this dogma of equality is simply ridiculous. For example, when I experimented on just about the simplest animal available, flatworms, I learned to tell one from another. And Pavlov realized that his laboratory dogs showed plenty of individual differences. And the same also would apply of course to *Homo sapiens*. Individuals are different, and so are groups of *Homo sapiens*. Chinese culture and East Indian culture and African cultures are deeply different from white Western culture, and I wouldn't say that our civilization is better than theirs. But it's nonsense to pretend that we're all the same.

In the context of that argument, Bertalanffy instructed his students that "the question about IQs between Negroes and whites is rather irrelevant." He was referring to the controversy ignited in 1969 by the *Harvard Educational Review* article of Arthur R. Jensen, an educational psychologist at the Berkeley campus of the University of California. Jensen reported that blacks generally score lower than whites in IQ tests. Bertalanffy used the word "irrelevant" because he recognized that academics could argue indefinitely about the question of IQ-test cultural biases and other factors relating to the interpretation of Jensen's data. Meanwhile, Bertalanffy cautioned, the Jensenite controversy tended to divert attention from the priority question of how best to nurture individual excellence wherever it is found in the human family.

In Bertalanffy's view, the nurturing of individual excellence—the opportunity to *exercise* the democratic right to equal opportunity—was being undermined by the distortion of democracy represented by the myth of equal merit. In his words: "The idea that individual differences don't amount to much is one of the consequences of behavioristic, stimulus-response psychology and its robot model of man and principle of environmentalism." He identified *environmentalism* as the idea that the human being is a *tabula rasa*—the blank slate pictured by English empiricist-philosopher John Locke (1632–1704)—and that adult personality is crucially determined by early childhood experience or by conditioning. For Bertalanffy, the classic expression of environmentalism was a widely quoted boast by behaviorism founder John B. Watson:

> Give me a dozen healthy infants, well formed, and my own specified world to bring them up in, and I'll guarantee to take any one at random and train him to become any type of specialist I might select—doctor, lawyer, artist, merchant-chief, and yes, even beggarman and thief, regardless of his talents, penchants, tendencies, abilities, vocations, and race of his ancestors.

In response to Watson's "guarantee," Bertalanffy wrote: "I do not doubt that Watson is correct; only the bunch will make very poor beggars, lawyers, and doctors indeed." In GST terms, Bertalanffy pointed out that we are open systems that *interact* with the environment, not open systems that merely are acted *upon*. We are people, not putty.

Bertalanffy did not advocate that we abandon the "all-men-are-created-equal" rhetoric entirely. Rather, he proposed to retain the notion in the form of an ethical "as if"—borrowing that term from *The Philosophy of the "As-If"* (*Die Philosophie des Als-Ob*) of German Kantian philosopher Hans Vaihinger (1852–1933). In an essay on Vaihinger, Bertalanffy explained: "According to Vaihinger's interpretation of Kant, [certain] idealistic concepts are fictions but nevertheless of immense importance: for we have to act 'as if' they were reality." Bertalanffy advised his students that human equality belongs in the category of Vaihinger's "as-if" in the sense that we should act as if all of us are created equal in the matter of being equally deserving of opportunity. But he warned that we should not allow that moral principle to blind us to individual human differences:

The present tendency toward pseudodemocratic egalitarianism, he said, must be replaced by "recognition of worthiness, of spiritual aristocracy, wherever it is found."

Bertalanffy was uncomfortably aware that his opposition to dogmatic egalitarianism could be misinterpreted as opposition to the spirit of democracy. And he knew that voices in support of his position were barely audible. He probably would have been gratified, therefore, had he lived long enough to read a 1981 article in *The Chronicle of Higher Education*, reporting on a Lisbon conference of the International Council on the Future of the University:

> A number of speakers took aim at what one called the "doctrinaire egalitarianism" that, they charged, had led to a reduction of standards and quality in several major research universities of the U.S. and Western Europe. In a paper on "Quality and Equality Reconsidered," philosophy professor John A. Passmore of the Australian National University said that the [1960s] demand for equality of opportunity had quickly turned into a demand for equality of result. He concluded that doctrinaire equality in those universities had devalued education for all students.

A World of Symbols

To complete his new image of humanity, Bertalanffy added what he believed to be the characteristic that makes us unique among all living systems: Humans create a world of symbols.

The first level of Bertalanffy's new image of humanity—our membership in the world of systems—we share with the likes of computers. The second level—our membership in the world of open systems—we share with the likes of plants. The third level—our membership in the world of symbols—we occupy exclusively. Though nineteenth-century essayist-historian Thomas Carlyle was wrong in defining us as tool-using animals—we share that trait with chimpanzees—we are unique in our creation and use of the mental tools called symbols.

From symbolism—*discursive symbolism* such as language and mathematics, and *nondiscursive symbolism* such as music and ritual—Bertalanffy traced the origins of civilization. He saw symbols as the heirlooms of our cultural heritage, as the insignia of our present and as the blueprints of our future. He regarded symbols as the creations of the human spirit, which in turn shape the human condition. All behavior that is specifically human, said Bertalanffy, can be traced to our invention of a symbolic world—from keeping up with the Joneses to taking an oath of poverty, from fashioning a vase to forging an empire.

Bertalanffy began writing and lecturing about his symbolic theory of human behavior in 1946, and the following year he gave a major public lecture on the subject at the University of Vienna. When he discovered that similar conclusions had been reached earlier in the century by two philosophers, Germany's Ernst Cassirer (1874–1945) and America's Susanne K. Langer (1895–), Bertalanffy began citing them in support of his own viewpoint. He noted: "In philosophic discourse, independent development of ideas is what comes nearest to scientific 'proof.'"

As a biologist, Bertalanffy saw symbolism as a product of the unique evolution of our brain—specifically, the marked increase in the mass and quality of our forebrain, from which has sprung human consciousness and culture.

Symbolism may have had its origin, Bertalanffy speculated, in primitive magic: "For primitive man, an image, be it material or acoustical, *is* the original, and gives him control over it. This is the essence of sympathetic magic. A puppet made from clay *is* the enemy, and the enemy can be killed if a needle is thrust into the image. Man takes possession of the world in symbolic images by naming things." Modern man was able to take possession of the world, Bertalanffy continued, because he discovered that he could use symbols for more than mumbo-jumbo. Modern man developed the symbolic "magic" of the *algorithm*—a system of symbols (an "alphabet") arranged and used according to a set of rules ("a grammar"), as with letters in language or numbers in mathematics. An algorithm such as the decimal system, or a similar symbolic system in geometry or calculus, is a conceptual calculating machine. Conversely, a computer is a materialization of an algorithm. Data is entered into the algorithm, the algorithm operates according to its "alphabet" and "grammar," and a result is produced which may have been extremely difficult to obtain, or even unobtainable, without the algorithm. The collective result of all our algorithms has been modern science.

Bertalanffy said symbolism generated an entirely new form of evolution. The evolution in biology, which occurs on a scale of millions of years, has been superseded in our world by the evolution in history, which occurs on a scale of decades. While the societies of insects and other creatures have remained unchanged for aeons, human society has evolved through scores of civilizations in the geological instant of roughly five thousand years. Symbols have enabled humans to perform stupendous intellectual feats, by engaging in risk-free trial-and-error experiments in our thoughts. We can test the future before it arrives. "Symbolism," Bertalanffy declared with poetic zeal, "is the divine spark distinguishing the poorest specimen of true man from the most perfectly adapted animal." A classic example of the relationship between symbolism and human consciousness—an example so apt that it was cited by Cassirer, Langer, and Bertalanffy—involved the transformation of seven-year-old Helen Keller from a deaf, dumb, and blind creature to a human possessed of and by symbols. Keller recalled the experience in *The Story of My Life* (1902):

> Someone was drawing water [at the well-house] and my teacher placed my hand under the spout. As the cool stream gushed over my hand, she spelled into

the other the word *water*, first slowly, then rapidly. Suddenly I felt a misty consciousness as of something forgotten . . . and somehow the mystery of language was revealed to me. I knew then that w-a-t-e-r meant the wonderful cool something that was flowing over my hand. That living word awakened my soul, gave it light, hope, joy, set it free! . . . Everything had a name, and each name gave birth to a new thought. As we returned to the house, every object which I touched seemed to quiver with life. That was because I saw everything with the strange new sight that had come to me.

The Helen Keller experience fascinated Bertalanffy because of her remarkably vivid recollection of her discovery of the symbolic world. Bertalanffy believed that those of us who take the realm of symbolism for granted are ignoring the most precious gift any human being ever receives.

To distinguish human symbolism from subhuman symbolism—a matter that was vital to Bertalanffy's image of humankind as a unique species—he defined symbols on the basis of three criteria that must be satisfied jointly.

First, symbols must be representative rather than merely expressive. Generally, this means they have content that's more specific than an animal's bark, growl, purr, or whimper, or spontaneous human cries of pleasure, pain, or panic.

Second, symbols usually are chosen without any biological connection to the thing that's signified. Human symbols, in Bertalanffy's terminology, are "freely chosen." Though some words may have been formed from related sounds in nature, the general rule is that there is no biologically enforced connection. "There is no biological reason," Bertalanffy noted, "why a certain thing should be called a *dog, Hund, chien, cane,* and so forth, according to the language in question."

Third, symbols are transmitted by tradition (education) rather than instinct. You can teach an old dog new tricks, but the dog won't teach them to its uppies. More to the point: though specific content is transmitted when a scout bee performs a "dance" that tells the other bees the direction of nectar (*cf.* biologist Karl von Frisch's *The Dancing Bees*), the ritual is purely instinctual. Even if human symbols are somehow rooted in instinct, Bertalanffy noted, they are unique to humans because we can make them and change them.

Bertalanffy emphasized the paramount importance of symbolism to human behavior by describing symbolism as a level of reality that is beyond both the material and mental levels of our existence. Levels of reality in GST, it should be noted, are not isolated compartments like those of the Cartesian mind and body. The levels of GST are *emergent*— mental from material, and symbolic from mental. But, though symbolic entities such as language and science are created by mental processes, Bertalanffy believed that the influence of symbolism can be better understood if we *regard* symbolism as a distinct (though not isolated) level of reality. In accordance with the principle of emergence, just as physical laws cannot fully explain mental reality, mental laws cannot fully explain the world of symbols. Bertalanffy concluded that the world of symbols must be governed by some systems laws that are unique to its own level. A goal that Bertalanffy set for GST, therefore, was the search for laws of symbolic systems, and the study of the interaction of the world of symbols with the worlds of mind and matter. Bertalanffy assigned this GST goal a high priority because he believed that symbolism is a two-edged sword that can cut both for and against us:

> Symbolic systems may become more potent than man, their creator. Then symbolic entities—status, religion, party, nation, what-have-you—may govern man and human behavior more strongly than biological reality. This is the basis of the most sublime achievements of man. But it is also the cause of all the follies of human history. Thermonuclear bombs are not only the ultimate weapon but the ultimate of symbolisms run wild in technology and politics.

139

The Value of Values

A part of the symbolic world that urgently needs our attention, said Bertalanffy, is the realm of values: enduring beliefs about desirable goals and behavior. Bertalanffy realized that, for many people, the subject of values seems irrelevant in an age of scientific "objectivity." He knew that the scientific and academic establishments generally sanctified and rewarded research and instruction that is supposedly value-free. But, like another scientist-philosopher of his time, Budapest-born physical chemist Michael Polanyi (1891–1976), Bertalanffy was convinced that values are decisive in all behavior that is uniquely human. In 1962, Bertalanffy told a symposium at Central Washington State College:

> In the last resort, it is always a system of values, of ideas or ideologies, that is decisive. It was an idea that founded the United States, even though little bands of settlers were fighting a mighty empire. An idea was victorious for the group of poor subversives called early Christians. Napoleon's soldiers, hungry and in rags, conquered Europe with ideas and determination. We have no reason to assume that this law of history has changed. Military hardware, including the most advanced superbombs, will not save us when the will to live, the guiding ideas or values of life, have subsided.

In Bertalanffy's formal definition, "values are things or acts which are chosen by, and are desirable to, an individual or to society within a certain frame of reference—cultural, historical, social, religious, etc." Thus, value may be assigned to a dollar bill, a Picasso painting, or the quality of mercy. Something may have negligible value for one society, like gold for the Aztecs, and precious value for another society, like the same gold for the conquistadors. A postage stamp may be worth a fraction of a dollar at the post office or thousands of dollars at a stamp collectors auction. In all cases, the criterion of deliberate choice is crucial, as can be illustrated by the fact that medals are given for persons who choose to rescue others from danger but not for the automatic response of rescuing themselves.

Modern society's choice of values, said Bertalanffy, is overdue for an examination. In almost every direction, he saw individuals and institutions being guided by destructive values, usually mechanistic, or by a nihilistic denial of all values. He diagnosed this crisis of the spirit as "the imminent breakdown of a symbolic universe of values." He saw the symptoms in such areas as economics, where money had lost its connection with such realities as gold or commodities; in politics, where democracy had lost almost all mutual meaning in the rhetoric of the Cold War; and in religion, where traditional churches had become social clubs while the hunger for spiritual values was exploited by promoters of cults. Bertalanffy was aware that many previous societies also had had crises of values, in the sense of conflicts and betrayals of belief. But he considered the contemporary situation uniquely ominous because widely shared values apparently no longer exist:

> When we look back, we find the greatest geniuses, from the Preacher in the Bible to Sophocles, Dante, Michelangelo, even Goethe, filled with the dismay about their times and expressing what modern philosophers would call existential anxiety: deep-rooted doubts about the meaning and goals of life. Nevertheless, we hardly are guilty of exaggeration when we say that there never was a deeper, more pervasive gap between the world which is and the world as it ought to be, a more profound insecurity as to where to go.

"A new symbolic universe of values must be found," Bertalanffy told a 1958 Caltech Conference on Science and Religion, "if mankind is to be saved from the pit of meaninglessness, suicide, and atomic fire." Melodramatic? Perhaps. But essentially the same sentiments were expressed by scientist-author Jacob Bronowski (1908–1974) in Bronowski's *Science and Human Values* (1956) and *The Common Sense of Science* (1958). The president of Johns Hopkins University, Steven Muller, was quoted in a 1980 interview with *U.S. News & World Report* as saying that a lack of values in scientific education is causing universities to turn out "potentially highly skilled barbarians." And, in 1981, in a milestone study of ethics called *After Virtue*, moral philosopher Alasdair MacIntyre wrote that we are living through a "new Dark Age," because our civilization lacks shared values.

In search of the lost universe of values, Bertalanffy journeyed into what he called "the most difficult, obscure, and controversial field in philosophy and behavioral science: the theory of values." The pursuit of a theory of values—a discipline called *axiology* (from the Greek word for worthy, *axios*)—was considered an important area of philosophy in nineteenth-century Germany and Austria. Its purpose: to examine values from the standpoint of their origin, meaning, and consequences.

In Bertalanffy's venture into axiology, he rejected the major existing theories. The *naturalistic theory of value*, that all human values spring from our biological needs, was dismissed by Bertalanffy because of its blindness to human values that he identified as biologically irrelevant (music) or self-destructive (martyrdom). The *ontological theory of value*, that all human values reflect Platonic ideals that have an existence completely independent of humanity, struck Bertalanffy as metaphysical and therefore of no use for scientific study. The so-called *humanistic theory of value*, that all human values are the expression of the individual's need for self-realization, was ruled out by Bertalanffy for failing to account for the many societies that placed a value on self-denial. A more sophisticated understanding of values, in Bertalanffy's view, could be obtained from the idea of *self-transcendence*. He told a 1970 conference on human values at SUNY Geneseo:

142

The realization of what appears to be specifically human is more than "self-realization" of the human individual. Rather it is self-transcendence—that is, realization of values going beyond [immediate needs of] the individual. This is the definition of every culture, from the most primitive taboos to the highest flights of art, science, and mystical religion.

An important characteristic of human values, said Bertalanffy, is that they share the tendency of all human symbols to develop an existence that transcends and sometimes masters their human creators. Humans produce values like spiders spin webs, but in our case the webs sometimes ensnare the maker. Bertalanffy advocated that values be viewed in the GST sense of value systems. Echoing Spanish philosopher José Ortega y Gasset (1883–1955), Bertalanffy declared that values tend to combine to form a hierarchical structure of belief, that this structure takes on a life of its own, and it must be studied if we are to understand an individual, a people, or an era. Bertalanffy identified his view as the *symbolistic theory of values*, based on systems of values as "symbolic superstructures created above the instinctual level" of behavior.

He suggested that we explore ways to restore a sense of values in education, science, and society. And he helped inspire and subsequently endorsed the value-seeking therapy of University of Vienna psychiatrist Viktor E. Frankl (1905–). Frankl, who declared his intellectual indebtedness to Bertalanffy, called his healing approach *logotherapy*, using the prefix *logo* to denote *meaning*. In books such as *Man's Search for Meaning* (1959), Nazi-concentration-camp-survivor Frankl described a collapse of values in modern civilization and a resulting existential neurosis arising from "a total lack, or loss, of an ultimate meaning to one's existence that would make life worthwhile." Frankl devised logotherapy (also known as *existential analysis*) as a way of helping each patient search for a system of values that would give meaning to that individual's life. The main conviction shared

by Bertalanffy and Frankl was that humans have a basic
need to relate to goals that are beyond those involved in
the goal of simple survival. In that connection, Bertalanffy
identified an "existential neurosis arising not from frustration of biological needs but from the meaninglessness of
life in modern society, a world in which values, purposes
and goals have collapsed and life becomes a senseless rat-
race." Bertalanffy offered a personal perspective on this subject during a classroom discussion in October 1971:

> When I transport myself back thirty years to the
> time of the Second World War, when I was living
> in Austria, I remember that we never knew from day
> to day whether we would be killed by bombs or put
> in a concentration camp. But we could see light at
> the end of the tunnel. We knew things couldn't go
> on like this forever and that this beast Hitler would
> be destroyed in one way or other. We knew this terri-
> ble period would end. We had something to strive
> for. We had hope. Nowadays the younger generation
> doesn't seem to have this feeling. Today there is no
> black and white of evil and good. There is no beast
> to conquer. Everything seems gray, and so there are
> no expectations.

Bertalanffy justifiably might have gone on to say, in the
memorable words of the old *Pogo* comic-strip: "We have
met the enemy and he is us." As Bertalanffy did go on
to say, the enemy is the shortsightedness of all humanity,
a condition that can be cured by a self-transcendent way
of thinking about human goals: general systems theory.

Because humans are beings with a unique need for such
self-transcendent outlets as religion, idealism, and art, Bertalanffy believed that the thwarting of those needs can be
as much a cause of pathology as the thwarting of needs
that are biological. Just as the health of mind and body
are interconnected in Bertalanffy's GST, so was there an
interconnectedness between the health of the individual and

that of society. He identified culture, therefore, as an important psychohygienic factor. He thus offered an insight about the idea of a *sick society*. A sick society, in the GST worldview, is more than a metaphor when the term is applied to the GST model of an organism-like society that is governed by systems of symbols, including values. "The diagnosis of a sick society," he wrote, "is quite simply that it provides more or less abundantly for the biological needs but starves the spiritual [self-transcendent] ones."

If health professionals began viewing us humans as the unique symbol-and-value-creating creatures that we are, said Bertalanffy, then some of the puzzles of mental illness might yield to new understanding. He credited existing orthodox theories of psychopathology for uncovering roots of mental illness that are biological and physiological, or related to experiences in early childhood. "But it seems to me," he wrote, "that these explanations omit or suppress a very essential thing: that which makes man into man, the symbolic world and the realm of human values." As an example of the symbolic component in mental illness, Bertalanffy cited paranoid delusions of grandeur, such as a person imagining himself to be Napoleon, and paranoid delusions of persecution, such as a person imagining that he is being followed by secret police. Some contributing factors of such illness may be biochemical, physiological and/or genetic, he acknowledged, but the *expression* is on the level of symbolism and therefore may yield to symbolic examination and reorientation. That is to say, some types of mental illness may be partly if not wholly the result of a disturbance involving a conflict between the individual's inner world of symbols and the outer environment of society. Another possibility is a clash between the symbolic world of society's values and the individual's inner world of values, or between either or both sets of values and the individual's biological drives. To fully understand the causes of mental illness, therefore, the therapist must recognize that mental disturbances may arise from factors in a culture. Bertalanffy believed that this may be especially relevant in dealing with disturbed members of social subgroups, such as the poor, the elderly, the ethnic minority, or simply persons who have become alienated from a particular cultural environment.

Bertalanffy's total contribution to behavioral science, in the form of "five Bertalanffian principles," has been summarized by GST psychiatrist William Gray:

> His insistence on an organismic or antireductionistic approach; his insistence that the psychophysical apparatus is characterized by primary activity that is antirobotic; his demand that an adequate general systems theory must concentrate on those characteristics peculiar to the human species, such as symbolism, which establishes an antizoomorphic position; his inclusion of anamorphosis and organizational laws at all levels as an essential component of advanced general systems theory, [which is] an antivitalist position; and finally, but in no way least, his demand that values are a necessary part of a new image of man and must be included in the development of advanced general systems theory, establishing an antimechanistic orientation.

In every respect, Bertalanffy's "new image of man" was an emancipation proclamation for the human spirit. It was a scientifically-based affirmation of the unique creativity of our species and of each human being.

Bertalanffy's "new image of man" was also an affirmation of our responsibility—to transcend distorted self-images that have tended to deny our humanity and that now threaten to deny our future.

6

A Science of Social Systems:
CAN WE FREE OURSELVES FROM THE PAST?

A major debt for any of [my] really insightful points goes to the late Ludwig von Bertalanffy. Indeed, almost everyone working in the general systems field would have to make a similar assignment.

John W. Sutherland, in the preface
to his *A General Systems Philosophy
for the Social and Behavioral Sciences*

In Bertalanffy's view, the social sciences were as much in need of a general systems viewpoint as the behavioral sciences. And, near the end of his life, he indicated that the need for GST in the social sciences had become urgent:

We know and control physical forces only too well, biological forces tolerably well, and social forces not at all. If, therefore, we could have a well-developed science of social systems, it would be the way out of the chaos and impending destruction of the present world.

That assessment is not exaggerated, judging from interviews I've conducted with persons whose job it is to think about alternatives to chaos and destruction. For example, the demographer who coined the phrase *zero population growth*, Kingsley Davis of the Hoover Institution, contends that industrial-world aid to hungry nations is setting the stage for famine-triggered global war by encouraging higher birthrates. He maintains that the only humane alternative would be a general systems approach in which we would make our aid to hungry nations contingent on population control, and in which the recipient governments would promote population control by linking it with incentives such as tax advantages and government allocations for local development projects. Though the Davis diagnosis and prescription are subject to debate, his viewpoint is illustrative of GST's relevance to dialogue about today's major social issues.

Bertalanffy believed that social science—by which he meant sociology, economics, political science, social psychology, cultural anthropology, archaeology, and history—should be pursued literally as "the science of social systems."

The Bertalanffian science of social systems would be based on the GST model of the social organization as an organism. His rationale was that social organizations are like living organisms in the sense that both display wholeness, interact with their environment, exhibit strategies of self-maintenance, and experience cycles of birth, growth, maturity, and decline.

In advancing an organismic model of society, however, Bertalanffy was careful to specify that it was only a model. He stressed that societies differ from actual organisms in one crucial sense: though the whole of society exists for the sake of its members, the holistic relationship in this case is not reciprocal. He said we must never forget that society is an entity created by and for individuals: "Man is not only a political creature; he is above all an individual." In the worldview of Bertalanffy's humanistic general systems theory, social organizations exist as a means to individual human ends rather than as ends in themselves. And each individual has an inalienable right to the pursuit of self-fulfillment.

But, having made that point, he would hasten to add that individual fulfillment cannot be achieved apart from society. For better or worse, we are social creatures. So, though we should not work *for* social systems, we must work *with* them. In the perspective of Bertalanffy's GST, freedom is a perpetual paradox. You can exercise it only on condition that it is limited. That's because one person's freedom tends to be another's restriction, as you can see from either side of such issues as rent control, gun control, and affirmative action. The whole world is a busy intersection in which you can cross securely only on condition that you are willing to wait your turn. And, to guarantee that you get any turn at all, you need a traffic system—which is to say, a system of social order. An absolutely free society would mean chaos and the end of what most of us would consider a free society. In GST terms, freedom can be achieved only as a continuous process of compromise: as a set of relationships within a dynamic system. The Bill of Rights cannot be applied absolutely, despite what some civil libertarians have contended. The right of a free press, for example, must sometimes be balanced against the right to privacy, the right to be protected against libel, and the right to a fair trial. The right of assembly must sometimes be balanced against the right to be free from harassment, as when Nazis demand the right to assemble in a neighborhood of Jews or when Klansmen choose to assemble amidst blacks. As the hippies of the 1960s discovered when they grew older, the dream of everyone's "doing his own thing" is a juvenile fantasy.

Assuming that the systems model of society is applied with its limitations clearly in mind, Bertalanffy recommended it as an extremely valuable tool of social thought. To the extent that social organizations behave *as if* they were organisms, he argued, their behavior may be scientifically studied and perhaps predicted according to general systems laws.

That view was transformed into a revolutionary 1966 textbook, *The Social Psychology of Organizations*, by University of Michigan social psychologists Daniel Katz and Robert

L. Kahn. In opposition to the conventional view that social organizations are the sum of their individual human members, and in opposition to the common practice of studying social organizations as if they are closed systems, Katz and Kahn adopted Bertalanffy's model of the social organization as an open system. They explained:

> The open-system approach to organizations is in contrast with common-senseapproaches, which tend to accept popular names and stereotypes as basic organizational properties and to identify the purpose of an organization in terms of the goals of its founders and leaders. The open-system approach, on the other hand, begins by identifying and mapping the repeated cycles of input, transformation, output, and renewed input which comprise the organizational pattern. This approach to organizations represents the adaptation of work in biology and in the physical sciences by von Bertalanffy and others.

Katz and Kahn expressed the view that the open-systems approach encouraged an awareness of the emergent qualities of social organizations and the profound ways that social organizations are affected by their environment.

In Bertalanffy's open-system view of a social organization, we are obliged to observe how it acts on its environment, how the environment acts on it, and how that interaction affects its growth and survival. For example, Bertalanffy suggested, insights from biological laws of growth and competition might be applied in the search for laws to predict and control growth and competition among nations and perhaps the cancer-like growth of urban blight, congestion, and pollution.

Another socially relevant characteristic of the open-system model, Bertalanffy believed, was the concept of inner-directed goals. To the extent that social organizations behave like open systems, said Bertalanffy, they may develop goals for the enhancement of the system itself. We must be constantly alert, therefore, to correct social systems whose goals become contrary to the purposes of its human members. The most common example, he observed, was the organization that betrays the interests and values of its members in the course of satisfying its own urge for growth. In such situations, a corporation may expand into diversified enterprises that are beyond the expertise of its management; a university may place a higher priority on the erection of new buildings than on adequate compensation for its professors; and a government agency may adopt or expand programs with no purpose other than bureaucratic empire-building.

Bertalanffy also offered the GST sociological approach as a perspective on today's frustrating social riddles about technology. He asked, for example, why we can jet across the nation, yet we must crawl across town. If we can supply wholesome air for astronauts, why can't we do the same for those of us who remain on Earth? Why, with all our awesome medical equipment, do millions suffer from medical care that is pathetically primitive? The answer, said Bertalanffy, is that the current *technological* systems approach needs to be expanded to a *general* systems approach, one that views technology as part of a complex social environment and that deploys technology on behalf of human values.

We also lack a general systems approach, Bertalanffy observed, in the realm of economics. America's economic system has been in constant trouble, he contended, because national economic policies have been too often adopted without sufficient anticipation of the reaction of sectors within and outside the nation. Along with GST economist Boulding, Bertalanffy found it remarkable that economics, a discipline committed so deeply to solving the problems of systems, should be so lacking in systems sensitivity.

The futility of fragmented approaches to social problems was a frequent topic of Bertalanffy's SUNY Buffalo lectures on GST:

It's completely ridiculous that it takes a couple of tons of automobile to bring my 165 pounds from my home five miles away to this campus each day. Everyone knows that the answer is the expansion of mass transit. But the government does not do what is necessary because of opposition from highway lobbies, auto lobbies, and auto-industry unions. We're not going to solve this problem until somebody uses the general systems approach of dealing with the whole network of interrelationships.

Lest there be any doubt about what Bertalanffy meant by a general systems approach to urban problems, he stressed that a really effective response to the transportation problem would depend on an integrated approach to all the major problems of urban life, including pollution, poverty, crime, and sanitation. He was aware of how frequently society's leaders have succumbed to the temptation to alleviate one problem at the expense of another, playing the classic political shellgame. For example, one level of government reduces taxes which must then be collected, perhaps with less efficiency and fairness, by another. A GST-wise electorate would not be likely to fall for such ersatz tax reform.

Nor would a GST-wise electorate be likely to go on falling for the traditional campaign promise to "get tough" on crime. If the problem of criminal violence could be solved by simply writing tougher laws and building more prisons, society would have brought this problem under control centuries ago. Tougher laws are meaningless to offenders who count on the excellent odds that they won't get caught, and these laws quickly reach a point of diminishing returns because the increase in penalties tends to increase the reluctance of defendants to plead guilty, of witnesses to testify, and of juries to convict. As we build more prisons, we multiply the number of convict recidivists. Most released convicts return to crime, frequently to more serious offenses, because imprisonment commonly weakens a convict's ties with his family, warps his sexuality, contaminates him with convict values, and sometimes converts him into an unemployable zombie. A GST approach would involve increased investment in our scandalously understaffed systems of parole and probation, increased investment in the professionalization of our law-enforcement agencies, and increased concern about environmental crime-contributing factors such as unemployment and inadequate educational, recreational, and family-counseling systems. Last but not least, the crime problem would be approached in terms of the rehabilitiation of society's system of values. The crime issue is a quintessential example of a problem that can be better understood if we view it in the perspective of Bertalanffy's conceptual model of the open system.

Until we approach our social problems with such GST insight, we'll be like the proverbial fool who rescues an endless series of drowning victims from a river without ever going upstream to learn who or what is pushing them in.

Bertalanffy's organismic-systems view of society, he noted, was consistent with independently developed contemporary systems approaches to social science, including the *integralist* theory of sociologist Pitirim A. Sorokin, the *systematic general theory* of sociologist Talcott Parsons, the *structuralism* of anthropologist Claude Lévi-Strauss, and the systems analysis of political scientist David Easton. In another relevant independent development, anthropologist Leslie A. White advocated a science of *culturology* that would study how human behavior is molded by cultural entities and how those entities are molded by cultural-systems laws.

In archaeology, Bertalanffy proudly cited published evidence of his influence on a movement called the *process school:* The associate curator of archaeology at the Smithsonian Institution, Kent V. Flannery, reported in *Scientific American* that the process school represents a determined minority of archaeologists who hope to revolutionize their discipline by "borrowing" Bertalanffy's GST approach. Whereas conventional archaeologists are content to piece together *descriptions* of prehistoric human behavior by studying unearthed artifacts, the process-school practitioners ambitiously seek *explanations* of prehistoric behavior by speculating about the prehistoric individual's adaptation to the various systems that comprised his world—ecological, agricultural, commercial, cultural, and religious. The process-school approach is based on the GST hypothesis that principles of social systems are common to societies of all eras.

Systems in History

If archaeology is a potential source of clues to systems laws that apply to culture, Bertalanffy reasoned, then an even richer source would be the vast field of recorded history. In support of that idea, he addressed the 1971 meeting of the American Historical Association on "A Systems Theory of History":

> I advance the concept of 'cultures as systems' as a working hypothesis, a conceptual framework for new empirical research. [I believe] it is a useful model [for] a science of culturology, opening new vistas and approaches toward understanding the phenomenon of civilization—civilization in general, and specific civilizations in particular—permitting a clearer view of problems like growth and decay, cultural autonomy and diffusion, civilization and primitive culture, and the like.

Because orthodox historians lack a systems view of history, Bertalanffy stated, too many of them tend to portray the human drama as a series of random wars and treaties, discoveries and disasters. And, because they dwell on parts rather than wholes, on isolated events and individuals rather than cultures, Bertalanffy believed that orthodox historians are forsaking the opportunity to collect valuable evidence of historical patterns that might reveal the laws that govern social systems.

Bertalanffy suggested that historians take their cue from scholars who have viewed cultures as organismic entities with distinct life cycles. He traced the concept of historical cycles back to ancient times, specifically to the rise and fall of cultures as described in the sacred Hindu texts of the Upanishads and to the historical writings of Plato and Aristotle. But he noted that the cyclic theory of history was first introduced explicitly in a 1725 classic, *The New Science*, by Italian philosopher Giovanni Battista Vico (1668–1744). Vico's book, a pioneering attempt to combine history and what amounted to sociology into what Vico called "a new science of humanity," examined cultures dating back to ancient Greece and Rome to show that human societies pass through stages of growth and decay. Vico's cyclical model, generally ignored in his own lifetime, was adapted by the French philosopher who founded sociology, Auguste Comte (1798–1847). Comte put forward the idea that cultures evolved through three stages: supernatural, philosophic, and scientific. Among subsequent subscribers to cyclic history were four Germans—Hegel, Marx, Engels, and Bertalanffy's favorite exponent of cyclic history, Oswald Spengler (1880–1936).

In Spengler's *The Decline of the West*, published in the wake of Germany's defeat in World War One, he expressed the pessimism of that time and place by picturing Western civilization as a cultural organism that had entered its final stage of entropy. Spengler's German title, *Der Untergang des Abendlandes*, actually referred to the "downfall" rather than "decline" of the West; and he blamed it on the Christian-democratic rejection of Prussian-style aristocratic elitism. He consequently became an idol of the Nazi militarists, until his opposition to the persecution of the Jews caused "a mutual disenchantment"—to quote William L. Shirer's *The Rise and Fall of the Third Reich*. Spengler remained in Nazi Germany, independently wealthy and politically aloof, until his death.

Though Spengler was a chauvinist rather than a humanist, he became an object of lifelong intellectual fascination for Bertalanffy. Perhaps that was because Spengler happened to be the subject of Bertalanffy's first publication, a four-part article for the literary section of a Viennese newspaper in 1923. Perhaps, too, the fascination arose from the fact that the young Bertalanffy had witnessed the post-World War despair that caused many central Europeans of the 1920s to be receptive to the idea of the downfall of the West. Be that as it may, Bertalanffy apparently never wrote or lectured about his systems theory of history without lauding Spengler for cyclic insights while dismissing Spengler's chauvinism as a personal eccentricity.

With respect, if not equal enthusiasm, Bertalanffy also frequently called attention to the contribution to cyclic history made by England's Arnold Toynbee (1889–1975). Toynbee produced a 12-volume *Study of History* (1934–61) that traced patterns of growth, maturity and decline in twenty-one civilizations. He too saw our civilization threatened by decay. But he said we could avoid that fate by eliminating the double standard of ethnocentric morality that separates races and nations and by forming a Christian-inspired, spiritually oriented world society.

Bertalanffy believed that many modern historians had rejected the cyclic view, dismissing it as poetry or fantasy, because a belief in historical laws would seem to contradict belief in free will. Confronting that concern, Bertalanffy made the point that historical laws would be no more enslaving than the laws of science, the knowledge of which obviously had liberated much of humanity from hunger, disease, and even physical isolation from other planets.

A belief in free will, Bertalanffy repeatedly explained, is not contradicted by a belief in laws of systems. The laws of systems are statistical, which is to say that they relate to *macro* levels, thus allowing for spontaneity of the individual. As GST theorist John W. Sutherland points out in his *A General Systems Philosophy for the Social and Behavioral Sciences*, a knowledge of *macrodeterminacy* serves the cause of free will by helping the individual deal intelligently with social systems.

With Toynbee, Bertalanffy held that humanity can acquire liberating knowledge from a study of past mistakes. With philosopher George Santayana (1863–1952), Bertalanffy held that only those who cannot remember the past are condemned to repeat it. With sociologist C. Wright Mills (1916–1962), Bertalanffy held that so-called historical fate often is actually a euphemism for obsolete social structures, and that we can improve our fate by changing those structures.

Bertalanffy's own hopes for the future were based on two phenomena which were not taken into account in the gloomy prognostication of Spengler. Unlike civilizations of the past, Bertalanffy pointed out, ours has developed the technology to triumph over age-old scourges such as pestilence and famine, and our civilization has the capacity to confront humanity's problems on a global level (if only we will). In Bertalanffy's view, we may be at the end of history's final cycle. We may be part of a cultural system that will die like all previous ones, in this case possibly in a war that ends civilization for good. Or we may escape such fate by being reborn into an entirely new historical experience: a world community, a functioning brotherhood of man such as that envisioned during the grim wartime days of 1943 by English natural philosopher Lancelot Law Whyte (1896–1972) in his little classic of hope, *The Next Development in Man*.

If civilization does get another chance, Bertalanffy said, we will face two further choices: a peaceful and prosperous world civilization in which every community and individual is alike, or a peaceful and prosperous world civilization in which there is still the joy of cultural and individual diversity and creativity.

Toward the end of his life, Bertalanffy was deeply concerned about humanity's future. He saw us sliding down a slippery incline toward the abyss of oblivion. But he believed we could stop our fall if enough of us assumed the responsibility for our civilization's survival. He believed there was still time to begin history anew. And he believed that meant we must take a fresh new look at the world's problems. We must stop focusing on villains and instead concentrate on wayward systems. That is not to say that he regarded individual leaders as completely innocent. But he had seen too much of the dark side of the twentieth century to believe that all would be well if only we could be rid of Hitler, Stalin, or some other demon on the dartboard of modern history. He had thought too deeply about the implications of the general systems approach to be distracted from the faults of the social whole by the faults of its individual parts. He was convinced that the only lasting answers to social problems lay in basic reforms of social systems:

> Contemplating contemporary history in the making, it is difficult to ascribe its irrationality and bestiality solely to individuals. . . . Events seem to involve more than just individual decisions and actions and to be determined more by socio-cultural systems. We know precisely what the effects of pollution, waste of natural resources, the population explosion, the armaments race, etc., are going to be. We are told so every day by countless critics. . . . But neither national leaders nor society as a whole seem to be able to do anything about it.

Clearly, he asserted in his *Robots, Men and Minds* (1967), humanity needs to devote much more attention than it has to the misdeeds of social systems. He pointed out that social systems such as corporations and governments have been given the power to act as if they are living persons—and they have been behaving as such—but they generally have not been subjected to the restraints of any personal code of ethics. Consequently, organizations continually get away with offenses that would be severely punished if committed by an actual person.

As a result of the unrestrained amorality of social systems, Bertalanffy maintained, humanity is in the grip of a dilemma. Though we have the technology to vastly improve the human condition—for example to eliminate hunger—that know-how is not being sufficiently applied. Instead, we live in a world with simultaneous food surpluses and famine. American farmers are rewarded with subsidies for growing tobacco. Soviet agricultural programs must compete with the gargantuan budgetary appetite of that nation's military establishment. And, in part of the Third World, merchants sell home-grown food overseas while their countrymen go hungry. The fault, as viewed from the perspective of Bertalanffian GST, is not in our stars and not entirely in ourselves—but substantially in our systems.

That theme was developed in some detail by an admirer of Bertalanffian thought, psychiatrist Judd Marmor. In an essay on humanity's future, in Marmor's *Psychiatry in Transition* (1974), he argued that the main challenge of psychiatry today is to identify and thereby help correct those forces in social organizations that drive perfectly "normal" people to commit acts that constitute environmental and military threats to human survival. Marmor recommended that our understandable concern about dangerously sick individuals who commit senseless acts of violence should be matched by a concern about dangerously sick social institutions.

Bertalanffy viewed contemporary civilization as if it were a person suffering from the symptoms associated with the label schizophrenia: split personality, persecution complex, delusions of grandeur, and general disintegration and loss of contact with reality.

That approach to destructive social behavior, it should be emphasized, represented a rejection of the common tendency to attribute atrocious behavior of an individual or group to the individual or group's ethnic identity. Bertalanffy was aware that, all too frequently, we react to this or that headline atrocity by observing, in effect: "It's just like *those* people to act so despicably." Bertalanffy recognized that the problem with human social behavior is the problem of human society in general. It is a problem not just about *them,* but also about *us,* as he explained to a SUNY Buffalo class in the fall of 1971:

Now mind you, if I am illustrating what I am going to say by contemporary examples, then it is not so much a criticism of present politics and politicians, but rather is a matter of laying some sort of foundation for the typically human predicament. So you see, if this were not 1971 but, say 1941, I would be at the University of Vienna and should speak as I did to the extent it was possible about the criminal insanity of Hitler and the war. And if I would have been in America in 1945, I probably would have spoken about the criminal insanity of dropping atomic bombs, for a very dubious and passing political advantage as against Russia. And if I would talk today not in Buffalo but in Moscow, I would have umpteen reasons for criticism, only I supposedly would have to be very careful not to find myself in Siberia or a lunatic asylum. So we in America have to be thankful, because we have preserved the right to speak.

He proceeded to exercise that right by applying the split-personality analogy to our society—accusing our society of preaching individualism but practicing computerized collectivism, transplanting hearts to preserve life but sending most cardiac patients to assembly-line hospitals, complaining that Johnny can't read while shortchanging Johnny's educational system, boasting of moonwalks while nurturing astrology, and denouncing crime while condoning the proliferation of handguns.

He also identified sociological expressions of the schizophrenic persecution complex. In the Cold War, he noted, one side sees most of the world's problems as the result of a conspiracy of godless communists, the other as a result of a conspiracy of ruthless capitalists. He said both sides were exhibiting delusions of grandeur similar to "the Germans saying that they will save the world, or the British saying that they are the race predestined to dominate the Earth." Turning to the Third World, he accused nations in those areas of losing contact with reality by practicing a dangerously obsolete form of nationalism:

> Take this question of nationalism. You know, if there was one laudable result of the terrible slaughter of World War One and Two, it was the *rapprochement* among some European nations who, after thousands of years of struggle, came to the conclusion that they could preserve their cultural identity while cooperating economically and in some ways politically. Now, just when humanity has taken those first steps to overcome the idiotic ethnocentric nationalism between nations like France and Germany, we see the new ethnocentric nationalism awakening in places like Africa, Asia, and the Middle East, with the possibility of a Third World War starting on the basis of any of those nationality struggles.

One approach to the prevention of war, in Bertalanffy's view, is the study of symbolism. That suggestion is easily misunderstood, judging from a brief reference to it in *The Year 2000*, a 1967 book by Hudson Institute futurologists Herman Kahn and Anthony J. Wiener. They ridiculed what they described as "speculations of Ludwig von Bertalanffy, the biologist and founder of general systems theory, to the effect that speech causes war because only animals with speech [that is, humans] go to war." In response to their own unknowing distortion, they wryly observed that persons who want to prevent war would find it "radically difficult to eliminate speech."

The Kahn-Wiener version of Bertalanffy's thesis was more than somewhat wide of the mark. Bertalanffy's actual thesis involved symbolism rather than just language, and his concern was that humanity learn to understand that symbolism can be not only a cultural boon but also a cultural bane. Symbolism makes us more creative than any animal, he said, but it also makes us more dangerous. He said our primitive biological drives can be grossly magnified and distorted by such symbolistic behavior as the reification of abstractions like national honor or destiny. He told a 1956 meeting of the American Psychoanalytic Association:

> If Hitler or Stalin had been ordinary murderers running amok, they would have killed perhaps a dozen people before they were apprehended. What made Nazism and Stalinism so pernicious was that such destructiveness was within a symbolic framework of ideology. The specifically human danger is the coupling of agressive instincts with constructs at the symbolic level.

He did not proceed, however, to recommend (as suggested sarcastically by Kahn and Wiener) that speech or any other aspect of symbolism be eliminated. Instead, he advocated that the sword of symbolism be beaten into a ploughshare:

> Symbolism cuts both ways. On the one hand, it leads to the most catastrophic manifestations of aggression, such as ideological warfare; on the other hand, it may be able to check the aggressive tendencies in man. It may do so either by morals and religion, or by transference from the biological to the symbolic level, as when killing the enemy is replaced by a rather mild form of aggression such as economic competition or playing chess or bridge.

He could have added such alternatives to homicidal conflict as the Olympics, psychodrama, civil litigation, and debates in the United Nations. He could have spent his entire life, quite justifiably, cultivating that one insight—the possible use of symbols to distract us from self-destruction. But he was obsessed with the human condition in its totality— unfortunately for single issues, fortunately for his many-faceted legacy of humanistic science and philosophy.

At any rate, assuming Bertalanffy was right about the role of symbolism in human aggression, then many behavioral scientists have been dwelling on the wrong aspects of the problem. Instead of concentrating on the biological instincts highlighted by sociobiology and the psychological factors of primitive or infantile regression highlighted by Freudian analysis, they should be focusing on a restructuring of our symbolic environment. And perhaps, as Norman Cousins suggested in his *Human Options* (1981), a beginning would be the promotion of some symbols for humanity— say, an international anthem—to match the emotional appeal of national anthems and other symbols of nationalism. A development of that sort, of course, would depend on cooperation from the world of education. In that regard, Bertalanffy endorsed the recommendation of his friend, Nobel biochemist Albert Szent-Györgyi, that the greatest good that education could do today would be to instill a trans-national awareness that all humanity is now part of one global system. In Bertalanffy's GST view: "Possibly the model of the world as a great organization can help to reinforce the sense of reverence for the living which we have almost lost in the last sanguinary decades of human history."

Peace Research

Bertalanffy undoubtedly would have been gratified to know that his contribution to a science of social systems helped inspire a discipline called *peace research*. According to his wife, he died without any knowledge of that development.

Peace research is the application of general systems approaches to the prevention of war. Instead of focusing on specific international problems and personalities, peace researchers widen their perspective to the international system of which the various problems and personalities are interacting components. As an emerging discipline, peace research is practiced by a loosely knit community of scholars who differ widely in ideology and technique but who generally share Bertalanffy's uncommon sense of sociological interaction and C. Wright Mills' view that the nuclear arms race is the epitome of "crackpot realism."

Peace research pioneer J. David Singer, a University of Michigan political scientist, has written a number of articles and books, including *Deterrence, Arms Control, and Disarmament* (1962), in which he examines international politics in the perspective of Bertalanffy's GST. Singer concludes that, rather than dwell on the transgressions of individual nations and leaders, we must concentrate on reform of the international system within which nations interact.

Another peace-research pioneer, "macro politics" scholar Charles A. McClelland, credits Bertalanffy for inspiring his decades-long search for systems patterns in international behavior. McClelland's interest in GST was ignited in 1954 by a Bertalanffy prospectus for the founding of the Society for General Systems Research. McClelland recalls: "The contact with the systems concept put together programmatically in my mind a lot of erstwhile disconnected phenomena of international relations." McClelland, who served as president of the Society for General Systems Research during 1961–63, directed a 1968–73 research project in which he used a GST approach to forecasting Cold War crises: the World Event Interaction Survey (WEIS). With funding from the Department of Defense, McClelland and his research staff culled masses of newspaper data about Cold War tensions, searching for patterns of behavior that might signal the onset of flareups. McClelland realized that WEIS was as fallible as weather forecasting, considering that both pursuits dealt with numerous shifting variables. He candidly described the WEIS objective, therefore, as an attempt to develop skill in determining "which way the wind is blowing." Looking back on the project a few years after its completion, he commented: "Research enterprises such as WEIS merely kicked the ball onto the field. The game is now."

A more formidable ball, still in motion today, was kicked onto the field of peace research in the 1950s by another Bertalanffy-inspired scholar, Stanford University political scientist Robert C. North.

North's peace-research story began during World War Two, when he resolved to study the causes of war as a result of being involved in the Japanese-American conflict in the Pacific. After the war, as a Stanford graduate student and then as a scholar at Stanford's Hoover Institution, North spent about a decade in an unsuccessful search for a theory that would explain how wars originate. Then, by chance, he read an article about GST, relating Bertalanffy's organismic concepts to the work of economist Boulding and physicist Schrödinger. Though North had never heard of GST or any of those three gentlemen, he was profoundly affected by the article:

> Those organismic ideas struck me like a proverbial thunderbolt. If they applied to human beings and their work—including nations and the international system—then it could be misleading to focus upon the Soviet Union and the People's Republic of China, *per se*. Rather, one needed to look at processes, interactions, relationships, interdependencies, flows—the behaviors of numerous variables relating numerous actors under a considerable range of different conditions. But what variables? What interactions? What relationships?

In search of the answers, political scientist North studied Bertalanffian systems literature, which he found in Stanford's library of biology. North consequently conceived of a pilot GST study of the pre-World War crisis of 1914, for which he obtained a grant from the Ford Foundation. With a small research staff, he began in the fall of 1958 to collect relevant historical documents, and then he subjected the data to content analysis. He subsequently saw a need to extend the project to questions about the violence-inducing interaction of European nations during the period extending backward from 1914 to 1870. That meant more grants, more staff, and many more years of work.

The project finally culminated in a 1975 book co-authored by North and one of his doctoral-candidate colleagues, a young woman named Nazli Choucri. The book, examining World War One as "a particular illustration of the dynamics of conflict and warfare, and of the role of national growth and expansion in predisposing nations toward violence," was entitled *Nations in Conflict: National Growth and International Violence.* Its principal thesis:

> Growth can be a lethal process. Despite proclamations of nonintervention or even genuinely peaceful intentions, a growing state tends to expand its activities and interests outward, colliding with spheres of interest of other states. . . . We [therefore] conclude that the probability of war will not be significantly lowered by goodwill alone [or] by deterrence . . . detente [or] partial limitations of armaments. Today . . . it is crucial to consider the world as a whole . . . to consider whether certain types of growth may be less conducive to antagonistic competition and violence than others, and to design . . . new ways of allocating technology, resources and markets for all the world.

North and Choucri take notice of the fact that there has always been an explosive potential in the interaction of population growth, technological innovation, and increasing demands for resources. But they argue that such historical forces can no longer be taken for granted. These forces must now be subjected to scientific study so that the interaction may be brought under control, they maintain, because growth collisions have become more likely than ever at the same time that they have become potentially suicidal.

Bertalanffy's posthumous influence over peace research was demonstrated again when North's collaborating graduate student, Choucri, became a professor at Massachusetts Institute of Technology, and she in turn became the mentor of Richard Kent Ashley, an international relations doctoral candidate with a Bertalanffian bent. Ashley recalls: "I was originally introduced to Bertalanffy's general systems theory and its relevance to political systems while I was an undergraduate in political science at the University of California at Santa Barbara. General systems theory has been part of the grammar of my thinking ever since." Discovering what Choucri and North had done with systems insights in their landmark study of World War One, Ashley devoted his 1977 MIT doctoral dissertation to what might be considered a sequel: a study of the growth, rivalry and balance of power of the Sino-Soviet-American triangle. Three years later, he published an expanded version of his dissertation, *The Political Economy of War and Peace*, in which he maintained that the leaders of the three superpowers have been pursuing goals that are rational in a narrow and nationalistic sense but suicidally irrational in the wider perspective of the global system.

Ashley, (now at Arizona State University) tells me that his research on the contemporary situation seems to confirm the North-Choucri hypothesis that wars are generally caused not by such relatively simple factors as ignorance or instinctual aggression but by complex interactions generated by the prevailing tendency of nations to grow and expand their interests beyond their borders. He reports that he has shared such ideas at the International Political Science Association Congress in Moscow in 1979 and at the West German-sponsored Berlin Conference on Large Scale Global Modeling in 1980. "Judging from my conversations with social scientists in the Soviet Union and other nations," he says, "I have some optimism that peace research has an important contribution to make, even if it does nothing more than encourage international dialogue that replaces mutual accusations with mutual attempts to understand what the causes of conflict really are."

In the line of intellectual descent from Bertalanffy, thirty-five-year-old Ashley regards himself as a member of the fourth generation. He cites the fact that he was the student of a student of a student of Bertalanffy's general systems theory: "Though peace research hasn't yet evolved into a full-fledged science, I see reason for hope in the fact that some of my students are part of a fifth Bertalanffian generation."

Meanwhile, the goals of peace research are also being served by some members of the first generation. A book by Rapoport, *The Big Two: Soviet-American Perceptions of Foreign Policy*, documented the urgent need for Soviet and American leaders to view both nations as part of an organismic system afflicted with a cancerous arms race. GST philosopher Ervin Laszlo has written *A Strategy for the Future: The Systems Approach to World Order*, and he has become director of the UN Program on Regional and Interregional Cooperation in the 1980s. Kenneth Boulding and his wife Elise, who is Dartmouth's sociology chairperson, were instrumental in forming a peace-research clearing house at Kent State University (the Consortium on Peace Research, Education, and Development). The Bouldings also have helped spearhead a campaign for Congressional establishment of a "West Point for peace," a national peace academy that would provide conflict-resolution training to future leaders of government and the private sector.

The principal tool of today's peace researchers is Bertalanffy's general systems approach, enhanced by computer modeling, simulation, and forecasting. Though peace researchers differ considerably in specific methodology, they all seek a way to balance competing national goals with the overriding goal of survival for the whole of humanity. In that sense, they are acting in the spirit of one of the most neglected major documents of modern history: the

"Strategy of Peace" commencement address delivered on June 10, 1963 at the American University in Washington, D.C., by President John F. Kennedy. Having gone to the brink of World War Three during the Cuban missile crisis eight months earlier, JFK called for a reexamination of our attitude toward peace:

> Too many of us think it is impossible. But that is a dangerous, defeatist belief. Let us focus on a practical, attainable peace, based not on a sudden revolution in human nature but on a gradual evolution in human institutions, on a series of concrete actions and effective agreements which are in the interest of all concerned. . . . So let us not be blind to our differences, but let us also direct attention to our common interests and to the means by which those differences can be resolved. And if we cannot end now our differences, at least we can help make the world safe for diversity. For, in the final analysis, our most basic common link is that we all inhabit this planet. We all breathe the same air. We all cherish our children's future. And we are all mortal.

Underlying JFK's Strategy of Peace and the efforts of peace researchers is the belief that the human race can act harmoniously when it perceives itself as a single system. An inspiring example that neither Kennedy nor Bertalanffy lived to witness was the World Health Organization's global eradication of the scourge of smallpox, achieved as a result of a ten-year (1967–77) teamwork effort involving the United States, the Soviet Union, and the Third World. The total cost of that victorious war against one of humanity's oldest and harshest enemies was approximately $500 million, a tiny fraction of what some nations spend each year for defense against other nations.

*　　*　　*

What could be construed as a special legacy for peace researchers was discovered in Bertalanffy's literary estate by his son, Dr. Felix Bertalanffy. It was a rough draft of an article that drew upon the elder Bertalanffy's knowledge as a collector of pre-philatelic documents to chronicle the evolution of the world's modern postal system from its apparent origins in fourteenth-century Italy. In Felix's introduction to his edited version of the article, for the *Postal History Journal* of January-May 1973, Felix noted that, though the author's original intent would forever remain obscure, the article put forward a significant example of international harmony: "Up to the present day, it is almost the sole truly international system mankind was able to develop that functions with worldwide cooperation, without major friction or conflicts." Indeed, the article showed how nations can function together as a global system when they pursue a mutual goal. We thus are left with a tantalizing question: If the nations of the world can see the mutual benefit of delivering each other's mail—to say nothing of eradicating smallpox—is it too much to hope that they can learn to see the mutual benefit of survival?

7

The Ultimate GST:
TOWARD A
UNITY OF SCIENCE

A theoretical and methodological program called general systems theory—presented in its fullest and most persuasive form by Bertalanffy—is an extension of the tenets of organismic biology. It is an attempt to provide a common methodological approach for all of the sciences, based upon the idea that systems of any kind—physical, biological, psychological, and social—operate in accordance with the same fundamental principles.

"Philosophy of Nature,"
Encyclopedia Britannica

Of all Bertalanffy's contributions to modern thought, his most daring was his proposal for a general systems discipline—the original meaning of his GST—that would strive to unify science by seeking models, principles, and laws for systems in general.

In common with other scientific pursuits, Bertalanffy's proposed discipline would seek explanation, prediction, and control. But, because a GST discipline would be without disciplinary limits, it would hold the promise of an unprecedented revolution in humanity's control over its own destiny. If successful, a GST discipline would produce what Bertalanffy called a holistic paradigm, consisting of universal patterns of organization that would serve as master keys to knowledge.

Having begun his systems thinking as an organismic biologist, he envisioned GST as the pursuit of what he called "the ultimate generalization of the organismic conception," an examination of the potentially universal applications of such biological concepts as the model of the open system, the principle of emergence, and the natural law of growth.

Bertalanffy's faith in the feasibility of a GST discipline was based on the abundant evidence that the universe is a cosmos rather than a chaos, a symphony rather than a cacophony. All matter is composed of atoms, and all objects are subject to gravity. All life is composed of cells, and all species are subject to the same genetic code. Everywhere in the universe, there is organization in the form of systems: complexes of element in interaction. Therefore, he asked, isn't it likely that all systems respond to some basic laws of organization?

To be sure, the unification of science is a dream that also has been entertained by scientists of the mechanistic persuasion. They have sought to understand phenomena on every level by reducing them to explanations in terms of physico-chemical laws. But Bertalanffy said science can never be unified in those (reductionist) terms because each level of existence manifests its own emergent qualities. Just as a wheelbarrow cannot fully explain a jetliner, an atom cannot fully explain an amoeba, and an ape cannot fully explain a human. Bertalanffy believed, however, that all levels of reality mirror a universal pattern of wholeness, of natural laws of organization—and that we can achieve an authentic unity of science by applying general systems laws while taking into account the principle of emergence. He anticipated that a GST discipline would determine "which principles are common to the several levels of organization, and so may legitimately be transferred from one level to another, and which are specific, so that transfer would lead to dangerous fallacies."

A Science of Similarities

A Bertalanffy disciple in psychiatry, author-educator-psychoanalyst Silvano Arieti (1914–1981), suggested that

Bertalanffy should be known as the founder of "the science of similarities." That phrase was well-chosen, inasmuch as the credibility of GST as a potential science depends on its success in dealing with similarities. Bertalanffy called these similarities *isomorphisms,* by which he meant structural likenesses that reflect a commonality in the way the parts of a system relate to each other. For example, though no two things could be more unlike than a noun and a leaf, the noun relates to other parts of a sentence and the leaf relates to other parts of a plant in ways that Bertalanffy believed were isomorphic. Bertalanffy was intrigued by similarities of that type, because they hinted at systems laws prevailing in widely different domains.

If such interdisciplinary isomorphisms offer explanation and predictability, as do the laws of physics, then the GST discipline can qualify as a science. If the similarities uncovered by GST are vague or superficial and therefore of no real use, then the GST discipline is destined to be nothing but an intellectual hobby. Bertalanffy was acutely aware of that challenge. He often discussed it, as in the following recollection of some unfavorable academic reactions to his early GST-discipline advocacy:

> The proposal was received incredulously as fantastic or presumptuous. Either, it was argued, it was trivial because the isomorphisms were merely examples of the truism that mathematics can be applied to all sorts of things, and it therefore carried no more weight than the 'discovery' that 2 + 2 = 4 holds true for dollars and galaxies alike; or it was false and misleading because superficial analogies camouflage [important] differences.

In response, Bertalanffy had two main replies.

First, he himself was an implacable opponent of reckless analogizing, most notably an opponent of what he called the "nothing-but" fallacy that portrays organisms as nothing but machines. He continually warned of mistaking models for what they represent. Just as blueprints for a building do not equal the building, models of human behavior and human society are not the equivalent of humanity. He noted that theoretical models necessarily reduce reality to conceptual skeletons—too much detail makes a model unwieldy—so model-designers must always be aware of the risk of failing to include parts that are vital to a particular study. "Whenever entities are studied and compared," he wrote, "there are diversities as well as uniformities. Both must be given equal weight." He also cautioned against model-building as a scientific fad: "Enthusiasm for the new mathematical and logical tools has led to feverish model-building as a purpose in itself—an indoor sport—often without regard to empirical fact."

Second, having adopted that cautionary position, he saw no need to apologize for using models. For all their shortcomings, he regarded models as extremely valuable tools of scientific thought. An outstanding example, he noted, was physicist Niels Bohr's early-twentieth-century model of the atom, which resembled a solar system. Of course, said Bertalanffy, it was oversimplified to the point of mythology. Nevertheless, it helped scientists think about the mystery of matter, because the correcting of a conceptual model is one of the most productive of all strategies of science.

But, for GST to become an exact science, Bertalanffy realized, it would need to focus on similarities that could be translated into laws expressed in mathematics. Ideally, GST would produce laws as elegant as Newton's law of universal gravitation, which states that the force of attraction between two bodies is directly proportional to the product of their masses and inversely proportional to the square of the distance between their respective centers. Furthermore, Bertalanffy noted, mathematics could bridge systems knowledge in the inanimate world, where mathematical laws abound, with systems knowledge in the behavioral and social sciences, where precise and predictive scientific laws are still being sought. As a matter of fact, Bertalanffian

GST would place special emphasis on justifying the term science in endeavors that are as yet nothing more than behavioral and social studies.

Bertalanffy introduced his proposed new discipline, GST, as a science that would speak largely in the language of calculus. Bertalanffy thus became an exponent of *dynamic systems theory* or *classical systems theory*, the application of the so-called classical mathematics of calculus to describe the dynamic behavior of open systems. Calculus, in effect, is custom-made for GST because calculus is the mathematics of movement, growth, and change. Bertalanffy applied differential equations of calculus—which compute the rate at which one variable in a situation changes in relation to another at a given instant or location—to examine how open systems change in a given period of time, and to measure the degree to which one part of a system reacts to the behavior of another part. By using differential calculus, he was able to provide mathematical precision to such GST concepts as dynamic equilibrium (the steady state), the import of energy from the environment (negentropy), and self-restoration in response to external disturbances (equifinality).

Bertalanffy predicted that the open system would be his most fruitful model, and he urged that researchers in all fields assess its value in the interpretation of phenomena in their respective areas.

Another basic GST model, hierarchical order, suggested to Bertalanffy that many if not all disciplines could benefit from considering the possibility that, in any organizational hierarchy, there is a tendency toward increasing complexity (anamorphosis) and a correlation between increasing complexity and progressive differentiation, mechanization, and centralization.

The GST model of hierarchical order was a special challenge to Bertalanffy because he could not think of a way to apply this mental tool mathematically. However, he anticipated that the model of hierarchical order would someday yield to mathematical description as a result of theories yet to be developed. In the meantime, he took the position that verbal models have great scientific value as tools of thought—and he cited the verbal models of Darwin and Freud.

Though Bertalanffy and other advocates of the general systems discipline were unable to prove that any systems law actually applies to systems in general, Bertalanffy was able to identify some systems laws that were versatile enough to qualify as candidates for such universality.

The candidate with the oldest roots is the *law of probability*. It can be traced back to eighteenth-century mathematician Laplace, who defined the probability of a favorable outcome as the ratio of the number of favorable outcomes to the total number of possible outcomes. Thus, the probability of a coin coming up heads is one chance in two, and the probability of that happening twice in a row is one in four. The probability of rolling a six on one cubical die is one in six, and the probability of a double-six with two dice is one in thirty-six. Of course, probability mathematics is employed not only by gamblers but by actuaries, geneticists, and any other persons wanting to anticipate the probable outcomes of potential situations in various systems.

Other systems laws that Bertalanffy favored because of their interdisciplinary potential are *the exponential law, the logistic law,* and *the law of allometry.*

The exponential law, or law of natural growth, is a general law of growth or decay at a constant rate. On a positive level, absolute size increases exponentially, as with compound interest in a bank account, the reproduction of bacteria, and the Malthusian explosion of human populations. Negatively, the law applies to the decay of radium, the killing of bacteria by disinfectants, and the decrease of a human population where the death rate exceeds the birth rate.

The logistic law applies to exponential growth that is limited by some restricting conditions. For instance, a population increases exponentially with the increasing number of individuals; but if space and food are limited, the amount of food available for each individual decreases until the size of the population reaches a steady state based on available resources. Similarly, new freeways invite additional housing and industry that require more freeways and so on until that environment has run out of room for such expansion.

Allometry is the law of relative growth of components within a system. The biological principle of allometry states that relative growth of the parts of an organism takes place according to mathematical laws, with fixed growth ratios among parts and between a part and the whole. Bertalanffy, a leading researcher of growth in biology, confirmed the validity of allometry in cells, plants, and animals—as well as in biological evolution, as exemplified by evolutionary increases in relative brain size among mammals. In humans, an infant's disproportionately large head grows slower than its body, while its disproportionately small legs grow faster than its body. The principle of allometry, for Bertalanffy, was an exciting verification of an organizing force that imposes what he called "harmony" on a system of competing parts. He suggested that the principle of allometry might lend scientific predictability to studies of relative growth in social science, such as relative population growth of urban and rural areas during periods of urbanization or similar relative growth in categories of labor as a result of progressive occupational specialization.

GST's Debut

Bertalanffy made his first public presentation on behalf of a GST discipline in 1937, twelve years after he began publishing his views on organismic biology, as a guest speaker for a philosophy seminar of pragmatist-neopositivist scholar Charles Morris at the University of Chicago. The reception must have been cool or even hostile, judging from his published recollection that he feared *further* criticism of his GST proposal. Moreover, he was apprehensive that controversy over his suggestion might jeopardize his career in biological research:

> I feared that my reputation as an experimentalist would be damaged if my preoccupation with such highly theoretical matters was uncovered. Science was [largely] dominated by one-sided empiricism. Only experiments and the collection of data were considered scientific in biology.

In this relatively early stage of his career, Bertalanffy chose discretion as the better part of valor: "I left my [GST] drafts in the drawer, and it was only after the war that my first publications in this respect appeared." His very first GST piece, for the German philosophy journal *Deutsche Zeitschrift für Philosophie*, was an end-of-the-war casualty: it reached the proof stage just as Germany and the journal went under.

Having spent the war in German-occupied Vienna, Bertalanffy emerged in 1945 as something of a science-world Rip Van Winkle. According to his recollection:

> It turned out that a change in intellectual climate had taken place. I found that quite a number of scientists in different fields had thought on essentially similar lines. So the idea of general systems theory, after all, was not a personal idiosyncrasy or fancy as I had believed, but rather was one within a group of parallel developments.

His reaction to these developments was a classic case of ambivalence. Though pleased to see that interdisciplinary systems ideas were being discussed, he confessed in at least one public lecture that "it is irritating when such ideas are introduced as if they are new and their origin is conveniently 'forgotten.'" At any rate, he now had no inhibitions about identifying himself with the GST cause, which he proceeded to do in German-language journals in Europe and then in

English-language journals in America. Soon, he caught up with the vanguard of the GST parade, and his post-war irritation gave way to a gracious attitude: "Whatever I may have been able to contribute, [there is] plenty for others to do better. And I feel happy that a number of excellent men appear to be willing to do so."

Bertalanffy joined forces with some of those "excellent men" in October 1954, over a lunchtable at the Ford Foundation's newly formed Center for Advanced Study in the Behavioral Sciences in Palo Alto, California. He was among the first group of thirty or so one-year resident fellows, and he was lunching with three other Center fellows who were GST-oriented: physiologist Ralph Gerard, biomathematician Anatol Rapoport, and economist Kenneth Boulding. A year earlier, a GST article Bertalanffy had written for *Scientific Monthly* had prompted Boulding to write to its author:

> I seem to have come to much the same conclusion as you have reached, though approaching it from the direction of economics and the social sciences rather than from biology—that there is a body of what I have been calling "general empirical theory," (or general systems theory, in your excellent terminology) which is of wide applicability in many different disciplines. I am sure there are many people all over the world who have come to essentially the same position that we have, but we are widely scattered and do not know each other, so difficult is it to cross the boundaries of the disciplines.

During the lunch at the Center, the conversation drifted to the problem of crossing those boundaries. Boulding recalled the situation for me:

> One of us—I don't remember who—said why don't we start a general systems society? Gerard, who had some connection with the American Association for

the Advancement of Science, suggested we call an organizing meeting in conjunction with the next AAAS annual meeting, that December in Berkeley. His idea was that we would use the meeting to find out if anyone were interested. He reasoned that, if nobody came, then we shouldn't form a society. We all laughed about this, because none of us really wanted to do any work. So, around the table, we drew up an announcement and a sort of manifesto that we would publish in the AAAS program for that year. Our organizing meeting was attended by about seventy people, and there was a lot of spirited discussion about what the society should do. But what really clinched it was that, a few days earlier, some gentleman from Milwaukee, a total stranger, responded to our announcement by sending us a check for $500. Obviously, if we hadn't formed the society, we would have had to send back the check. So that's how we decided to form the society.

The organization was christened the Society for the Advancement of General Systems Theory. In 1957, the name was changed to the somewhat more modest Society for General Systems Research. The Society's manifesto defined a general system as any theoretical system of interest to more than one discipline. That definition was far less ambitious than the Bertalanffian vision of laws for systems in general, but Bertalanffy agreed to the compromise in the belief that even a thousand-mile journey must begin with one step.

The manifesto stated that the society's major functions would be to:

(1) investigate the isomorphy of concepts, laws, and models in various fields, and to help in useful transfers from one field to another;
(2) encourage the development of adequate theoretical models in the fields which lack them;
(3) minimize the duplication of theoretical effort in different fields; and

(4) promote the unity of science [by] improving communication among specialists.

Boulding became the first president, and the Society became an AAAS affiliate with meetings to be convened as part of the annual AAAS conventions. Eventually, there were chapters in many parts of the nation and in Canada, Mexico, Argentina, Chile, Colombia, Brazil, England, France, Germany, Austria, the Netherlands, Switzerland, Sweden, Czechoslovakia, the Soviet Union, Japan, India, Australia, New Zealand, South Africa, the Sudan, and Israel.

In 1956, Bertalanffy founded the Society's yearbook, *General Systems*. Co-editors Bertalanffy and Rapoport encouraged submissions of scientific papers from a wide spectrum of systems thought. In the preface to the first volume, the editors expressed the hope that the yearbook would serve the aim of the Society "to bring together areas of research with dissimilar contents but with similar structures or philosophic bases, so as to enable the workers in various fields to develop a common language and thus to stimulate each other more effectively." Contents of the first volume consisted of fifteen papers, including articles (by the four founders and others) on such topics as mathematical models in the social sciences, a general theory of growth, neurological systems, and a parallel between learning and evolution.

Bertalanffy remained co-editor until his death in 1972, by which time the yearbook had been established as a scientific forum with more submissions than it had space to publish. Rapoport remained at the editorial helm until 1977, the year of volume XXII. For that edition, Rapoport wrote a farewell preface in which he confessed that he could not define the yearbook editorial policy, because neither he nor anyone else could set limits to a field as broad as GST. With engaging candor, he wrote:

There being no general systems theory in the accepted scientific sense of the term, validation criteria could not be applied. Many papers bordering on far-out fringes of "conceptual experimentation" found a home in the pages of *General Systems*, whether deservedly or not, only time will tell. Unquestionably, the majority of them will sink into oblivion, as will the vast majority of all papers now published in the avalanche of the publication explosion. It may be some consolation to note that this explosion still does not match the extravagance of nature: out of some 85 million spermatozoa ejaculated in the human act of love, one occasionally produces a new life.

Though the yearbook today uses only scientific-journal reprints, the SGSR now also publishes a quarterly *General Systems Bulletin* as well as proceedings from the Society's annual meetings. Judging from those proceedings, the meetings are an interdisciplinary feast of biology, psychology, history, education, ecology, engineering, economics, mathematics, philosophy, medicine, and urban planning.

And, though the SGSR never grew very large—current membership is barely a thousand including those overseas—it has survived as a Bertalanffian beacon in what has become a vast ocean of systems science and technology. The SGSR has fourteen institutional members, including the Systems Science Institute at the University of Louisville in Kentucky (the Society's current home), the Humanistic Psychology Institute of San Francisco, and the Royal Library of Copenhagen, Denmark.

In 1980, the SGSR became a founding member-society of the International Federation for Systems Research, headquartered at Laxenberg, Austria. The president of both the SGSR and the International Federation, electrical engineer and systems-science author George J. Klir, is the chairman of the department of systems science at the School of Advanced Technology of SUNY Binghamton. That school is the site of the General Systems Depository of systems manuscripts and the editorial headquarters of the *International*

Journal of General Systems, which was founded in 1974 and is still being edited by Klir.

Another systems movement development—which Bertalanffy helped inspire and which his three SGSR co-founders joined—originated at the University of Chicago during the early 1950s under the leadership of a psychiatrist and former student of Alfred North Whitehead, James Grier Miller. Miller began this effort with an interdisciplinary group of colleagues who shared the goal of forming a general theory of behavior, and he coined the term *behavioral science* to describe their intention. In the preface of his 1978 text, *Living Systems*, he recalls:

> Our Committee [on Behavioral Sciences] began regular meetings in 1952. We were stimulated to undertake our activities by suggestions from physical scientists, among them Enrico Fermi and Leo Szilard, who felt a heavy responsibility for the fearsome developments in nuclear weapons, and who thought that, because [humanity] understood so little about why men fight and kill, the development of the sciences of man should be accelerated. They pointed out that natural science had advanced speedily after general theories were proposed and they suggested that we try a similar strategy. We were at first skeptical of the value of such endeavors, since we were aware of the primitive state of the behavioral sciences, the important disagreements within them, and the lack of common speech and understanding among them. Yet it seemed worthwhile to bring these divergent points of view together and begin to work toward the distant goal of common understanding. . . . As we talked together, a number of us began to see promise in the general systems theory proposed by Bertalanffy and others, and gradually our point of view was organized into what I call general living systems theory.

In 1953, Miller's discussion group became the University of Chicago's Institute of Behavioral Sciences. Two years later, Miller and several institute members moved to the University of Michigan in Ann Arbor, where they established the Mental Health Research Institute, the first interdisciplinary group formed to engage in a general systems approach to mental health and mental illness. Obviously, the Miller group now had a much wider scope than their original concern about "why men fight and kill."

Meanwhile, Bertalanffy's model of the open system was adopted by University of Michigan social psychologists Katz and Kahn. Significantly, they declared themselves to be GST disciples who believed that the best way to advance GST was to apply the open system model to one discipline at a time rather than make the direct attempt to prove GST's universality.

Regardless of when, if ever, GST unifies science, Bertalanffy felt it could serve as an approach to the integration of education. He therefore recommended that GST be viewed by academe as a current interdisciplinary systems science rather than just a potential science for all systems.

The present writer, having taught at four universities and having served on the public information staff at two of them, is quite conscious of the need for such interdisciplinary reform. Our civilization seems to be suffering a second curse of Babel: just as the human race builds a tower of knowledge that reaches to the heavens, we are stricken by a malady in which we find ourselves attempting to communicate with each other in countless tongues of scientific specialization. To borrow the terminology of psychologist Joseph R. Royce, the typical brilliant scientist of the 1980s has become "the encapsulated man." We cannot expect to be rescued by classical generalists; a latter-day Leonardo would be unable to keep pace with the proliferating knowledge in a single one of today's technical disciplines. Neither can we expect salvation from pure philosophers, now that technology is hurling answers at us, like recombinant DNA and test-tube baby-making, faster than we can frame questions. But an interdisciplinary systems science would give scientists, philosophers, and others an integrative perspective—a conceptual "pair of spectacles" through which to see how the fragments of the world relate to each other and to the world as a whole.

Here is just one example of the need for training scientists with a GST viewpoint: Oceans are among the most important of all natural systems, but there is virtually no systems approach to oceanography. The approach almost always is fragmentary: physical, chemical, geological, or biological. As a marine-institute oceanographer recently told me in an off-the-record conversation:

> If we can achieve a GST-style integration, we'll probably see dramatic progress in navigation, long-range weather forecasting, pollution control, ocean harvesting of food and pharmaceuticals, and perhaps ultimately the development of underwater farms and cities. But the first step will have to be the training of oceanographers who are really interdisciplinary.

Because no scientist nowadays can master a whole group of disciplines, GST may be applicable as a sort of transdisciplinary passport. As Bertalanffy put it: "General systems theory should be an important means of instigating the transfer of principles from one field to another [so that it would] no longer be necessary to duplicate or triplicate the discovery of the same principles in different fields."

That potential transfer of principles, in the opinion of Boulding, could turn out to be the most significant of all the fruits of a GST discipline. Citing his experience as a teacher of a general systems course, "General Social Economic Dynamics," for honors seniors at the University of Michigan, Boulding cites two main values for a GST approach in education: The discovery of interdisciplinary principles would spare the student from having to learn each discipline from scratch. And, perhaps more significantly, the student's intellectual interest would be enhanced with the perception that seemingly unrelated things are in fact related—"that for instance, the architecture of an insect is related to that of a building, that social evolution is in a very real sense a continuation of biological evolution with less random mutations, and that the automobile is a species very much like an animal but with a more complex reproductive process."

From the 1950s onward, Bertalanffy became an integrative education activist. He contributed articles to the journal of the Foundation for Integrative Education, which was dedicated to the "integration of all knowledge through the study of the whole of things." And, in 1962, he was among educators, including sociologist Sorokin and psychologist Maslow, who founded the New York-based International Center for Integrative Studies (ICIS). As related by ICIS literature, "the Center grew out of a deep concern about the trends toward overspecialization and fragmentation" and it has expressed this concern by means of seminars, workshops, lecture series, study tours, and an international correspondence forum. The ICIS director of research, J. Arnold Roze, an associate professor of biology at City University of New York, says he remembers Bertalanffy well:

> I must have met with him about two dozen times, beginning when he and I were helping to plan ICIS and continuing to his last years in Buffalo. I never knew anyone more dedicated to integrative education and more willing to buck the contemporary trend toward specialization. As the father of general systems theory, and as a fine example of the old European tradition of generalist scholars, Bertalanffy was one of the most important of all proponents of integrative education. You might say integrative education was his whole life.

Bertalanffy's opposition to academic insularity was far broader than that expressed by British physicist-novelist-educator C.P. Snow (1905–1980). In Snow's famous *Two Cultures* lecture of 1959, the focus was on the lack of communication between "the culture" of his fellow scientists and that of his literary colleagues, with special emphasis on what Snow regarded as anti-scientific provincialism on the part of "literary intellectuals." If literary scholars would learn about science, Snow suggested, then perhaps the Two Cultures could unite to heal social ills such as the global gap between "have" and "have-not" societies. In contrast to that view, Bertalanffy condemned the tendency toward insularity among all disciplines, and especially among the sciences. He saw the problem compounded by academic territoriality, with each specialty ferociously guarding its independent existence in defiance of the reality that all knowledge is interconnected. The wholeness of nature, he emphasized, cannot be seen from inside the walled citadels of the modern university.

Bertalanffy maintained that academic overspecialization cannot be overcome by simply asking science students to take some courses in humanities, and vice versa: "One can hardly expect a history student to get excited about the anatomy of the earthworm or a student of biology [to be entranced by] the Long Parliament." He advocated instead that educators prepare interdisciplinary courses from material carefully selected to highlight integrative *principles*. For Bertalanffy, a GST educational policy would produce professionals who, though they make their living as specialists, view the world as generalists. They would keep reminding themselves to remove their specialized spectacles so they could see the world as the whole that it is. And, as comprehensive thinkers, they would be concerned about know-why as much as know-how.

Contemplating the unsteady progress of GST as a would-be discipline, Bertalanffy sometimes defended it as a father might excuse an awkward child. He explained that GST is "still in a stage of beginning and grasping," and that we therefore should not be surprised to find it still "immature" and "inarticulate":

All we have are premonitions, semi-philosophical intuitions, a few principles remote from mathematical rigor in description and prediction. Developing principles that apply to systems in general is a task far from being finished. We are aware of the problem even though remote from its final and elegant solution. The program is clearly posed. Its elaboration has only begun.

In further defense of his brainchild, he wrote: "One should remember that the establishment of classical physics took some three hundred years from Nicole d'Oresme [the fourteenth-century French bishop who made a major contribution to the laws of motion] to Galileo and Newton. We have to be patient if the new trend has not yet reached the maturity of physics."

Of course, there is the possiblity that the GST search for universal laws of systems will turn out to be as futile as the centuries-old search of the alchemists for the universal substance of which everything else was supposed to have been made—the primal ingredient they thought would enable them to cook up such desirable concoctions as elixirs and gold. But, by the same token, perhaps GST explorations will be as productive as alchemy in the sense of pointing the way toward a whole new era of experimental science. We might well remember that philosopher Francis Bacon (1561–1626) compared alchemy "to the man who told his sons he had left them gold buried somewhere in his vineyard; where they by digging found no gold, but by turning up the mould about the roots of the vines, procured a plentiful vintage."

In the case of GST, though the golden goal of a universal systems discipline may remain out of reach indefinitely, the vintage of the GST worldview may be exceedingly plentiful. That hope was summed up by Bertalanffy in an essay that appeared in one of his posthumous collections of papers, *Perspectives on General Systems Theory:*

As happens with new ideas, those of the author were resisted or refused by [what science historian Thomas Kuhn called] "normal science." In fact, the author's life was a continuous uphill fight—he could have done better and furnished a less fragmentary product had he encountered less resistance during his productive years. He may say, however, that he was vindicated by the eventual outcome. The organismic conception, the systems outlook, symbolism as a basic human characteristic . . . are gaining ground [among many writers]. Premises, starting points, fields of interest and of research are different. And, owing to the enormousness of contemporary literary production, communication is difficult or absent, even with the best intention to know and appreciate one's intellectual allies. But with all these handicaps of personal biases, inadequacies and idiosyncrasies, a panorama is nevertheless developing where brush strokes fit together, complement each other, and begin to look like a grand vista. If this does not fit the [Kuhnian] picture of a scientific revolution with its breakdown of old and development of new "paradigms," it would be hard to find a better one.

8

The Systems Movement:

A FERTILE CHAOS

[One of the most] significant historical events in my lifetime was the growing together of a number of ideas we may [collectively] call cybernetics, or communication theory, or information theory, or systems theory. The ideas were generated in many places: in Vienna by Bertalanffy, in Harvard by [cybernetics pioneer] Wiener, in Princeton by [game theory pioneer] von Neumann, in Bell Telephone labs by [information theory pioneer] Shannon. . . . All these separate developments in different intellectual centers dealt with . . . the problem of what sort of thing is an organized system.

Gregory Bateson, *Steps to an Ecology of Mind*

Anthropologist Gregory Bateson (1904–1980), a leading systems thinker himself, was one of many writers who tended to obscure the differences between Bertalanffian GST and other systems approaches, some of which are quite alien to Bertalanffian philosophy. The confusion is understandable, when you consider the fact that this conceptual terrain is a semantic jungle. Theories about almost any technical system—computer, communication, information, etc.—are nowadays apt to be called systems theories, as if theories about one's relatives should be called relativity. Nearly any integrative or interdisciplinary approach to anything is liable to be called a systems approach. Often, it is called *the* systems approach, or even general systems theory. And authentic systems approaches that are as different from each other as apples and oranges are dished up to the general public as a single serving of fruit salad.

In an attempt at clarification, I herein refer collectively

to all actual systems practices and practitioners as the *systems movement*, a term used by Bertalanffy and his GST colleagues. To underscore the differences in origin and outlook between Bertalanffian GST and the various industrial-management-military systems approaches, I refer to the latter collectively as *systems technocracy*, a term I employ in a spirit of semantic desperation rather than literary pride. Throughout, I refer to pseudo-systems approaches not at all.

If one is permitted to entertain the notion that a systems movement truly exists as an entity, then one may say that this movement emerged in the 1950s. Continuing with that premise, one may surmise that the movement emerged at that time because of the interaction of three independent developments. The first was the accumulated intellectual impact of organismic-systems thinkers like Bertalanffy, evidenced by the appearance of forums of systems-science thought such as the Society for General Systems Research. The second development was the World War Two mobilization of interdisciplinary scientific defense teams by the governments of England and the United States, spawning the systems technocracy of *systems engineering* and *systems analysis* (also known as *operations* or *operational research*) in much of the industrial world. The third development was the postwar Second Industrial Revolution of automation, self-regulating machines, vastly complex engineering and communication systems for defense and space, and electronic computers that could calculate the very type of mind-boggling, multivariable problems of interaction that are posed by systems science.

Members of the systems movement are what Bertalanffy called "a heterogeneous lot." They are biologists, behavioral scientists, and social scientists. They are systems engineers, analysts, and designers. They practice management science and cost-effective analysis. They work for industry, consulting firms, universities, think tanks, government, and the defense establishment. They teach, lecture and write about their different views of the systems approach, and they share ideas by joining systems-science organizations and by attending systems-science conferences in many parts of the world. They champion general systems theory, cybernetics, information theory, game theory, and other variations of the holistic theme. They differ widely in training, methods, and philosophy. Some are organismic humanists; many are mechanistic technocrats. Some don't have the faintest idea what others are up to, some don't care, and some, like Bertalanffy, don't always like what they see. But, like it or not, they are all part of the same growing trend in certain spheres of science and society: a basic shift in emphasis from analysis to synthesis.

Bertalanffy had no illusions about the systems movement. He knew it was characterized less by consensus than by chaos. But he regarded it as "a fertile chaos"—prolific with insights and inspirations and nourished by an idea whose time has come: holism. He wrote: "This is a scientific revolution which, when considered in retrospect, may well equal the Copernican Revolution in importance."

The previous chapters of this book have dealt with the many Bertalanffian contributions to the movement, in biological, behavioral and social realms. But the most visible part of the movement, from the standpoint of the lay public, has been systems technocracy, as exemplified by systems engineering and systems analysis/operations research.

Operations research originated in the arena of military technology during World War Two in Britain, when that nation was facing a relentless onslaught from Germany. The British High Command recruited teams of physicists, mathematicians, and other scientific personnel to engage in "operational research" to improve the operation of radar networks and, subsequently, bombing squadrons, naval convoys, and other military systems. That approach was promptly emulated by the wartime military establishment of the U.S. and was also adopted for strategic weapons research by the Rand Corporation and other think tanks. During the 1950s, operations research, which then became known also as systems analysis, was extended to a wide variety of business and industry in the U.S. and abroad.

Today, systems analysis/operations research is a designation for a wide variety of professional methods of managing large and complex systems.

Along with the trend for systems engineering to overlap systems analysis/operations research, there is a trend for both to expand into behavioral and social areas, where they are interacting somewhat with Bertalanffian and other brands of GST. Systems technocrats are seeking ways to improve technological efficiency by maximizing the cooperation of the human components of systems—for example, to overcome human resistance to technological change. Also, systems technocrats are becoming interested in the possibilities of applying their efficiency procedure to social goals such as crime control, health care delivery, and aid to developing nations. This trend has produced still another interdisciplinary systems discipline, called *policy sciences*. A journal of that title was launched in 1970 under the editorship of Rand mathematician E.S. Quade. In his maiden editorial, Quade noted that policy sciences had arisen from the need "to bring the knowledge and procedures imbedded in the 'soft' or behavioral sciences into systems engineering and aerospace technology" and conversely "to introduce the quantitative methods of systems analysis and operations research into . . . social and political science."

The interface of systems science and social science is clearly evident in the prospectus of the Systems Science Institute at the University of Louisville, which was established in 1974 "to train graduate students in general systems theory . . . action research [with] emphasis on health delivery systems, energy systems, ecological systems, and social and behavioral systems."

In the world of business, the systems approach often is called *systems management*. Originating in some 1960s collaborative efforts of administrators in the U.S. Air Force and the aerospace industry, systems management tailors systems techniques to specific management problems. By comparison with conventional business management, systems management makes a special effort to base decisions on the study of a total system, including systemic interactions involved in short-term versus long-term results of a particular program.

An Array of Approaches

The multiplicity of systems professions is matched by what Bertalanffy called "an array of systems approaches":

> We intentionally use the somewhat loose expression "approaches" because they are different in basic assumptions, mathematical techniques, and aims, and they are often unsatisfactory and sometimes contradictory. They agree, however, in being concerned, in one way or the other, with "systems," "wholes," or "organization;" and in their totality, they herald a new approach.

Most of the time, Bertalanffy's attitude to what he called "this bundle of new disciplines" was quite cordial. He advised his readers that his systems approach might work well on some problems, other systems approaches might be more appropriate for other problems, and sometimes the best approach might be a combination. In that expansive mood, he endorsed a policy of the-more-the-merrier:

> There is indeed a great and perhaps puzzling multiplicity of approaches and trends in general systems theory. This is understandably uncomfortable to those who want a neat formalism, e.g., the textbook writer and the dogmatist. But the fact that "system theories" by various authors look rather different is not an embarrassment. It is quite natural in the history of ideas and science, and is particularly healthy in a new and growing field.

Eventually, Bertalanffy hoped, the productive approaches

would survive and coalesce in one congenial cluster of general systems science. He believed such integration might happen with the gradual discovery that one approach is a special case within another and that other approaches are complementary or even equivalent. In the meantime, he counseled, let's "follow up each model and see how far we can get."

A mathematical general systems model *par excellence*, according to GST biomathematician Anatol Rapoport, is *automata theory*. This approach explores the potential of computers by using a theoretical model of a computer that was published back in 1936 by English mathematician Alan M. Turing. His proposed computer—the infinite-memory Universal Turing Machine—was conceived to perform human-like calculations by scanning a tape with symbols that it could imprint or erase according to programmed instructions. Though Turing's dream of artificial intelligence has in some ways been realized now for decades, mathematicians continue to devise theoretical models of Turing's concept in order to explore future possibilities of the computational process. Practitioners of automata theory use it to help design future computers and also to seek insight into computational systems in general, including that of our own central nervous system. Computers perform their wizardry with binary digits or *bits* of information—"0" or "1"—as in the yes or no units of information in the parlor game Twenty Questions. Just as twenty yes/no bits in that game can reveal a fairly complex answer, a much more complex answer can be attained with bits that number in the millions, as in computers, or trillions, as in the human brain.

Computers are frequently used today for a systems approach called *linear programming*, in which the word *programming* does not refer to the instructions fed to a computer but to the older idea of programming as planning and scheduling. Linear programming, which is commonly used to help determine the most efficient allocation of limited resources such as manpower and matériel, was adopted by the U.S. Air Force in 1947, then employed widely by the military, business, and industry. The technique, also called *linear optimization*, uses linear algebraic equations to arrive at a quantitative description of the various key aspects of a system. Once the system variables are thus translated into mathematical terms, the equations are manipulated in order to maximize or minimize variables such as profit and loss. Linear programming depends on assumptions of linear, straight-line relationships: for example, the assumption that two factories will produce exactly twice as much as one. But two salespersons won't necessarily sell twice as many products as one, because the situation may be complicated by such factors as limited demand for the product, wasteful competition between the salespersons, and unequal salesperson performance. When such complexities exist in the system, the problem is translated into more complicated, nonlinear equations, in which case the procedure is called *nonlinear programming*.

The advent of the computer made possible what is now a very popular technique among systems researchers: *computerized simulation*. A mathematical model of a system (telephonic, transportation, etc.) is fed to a computer and then subjected to hypothetical challenges, stresses, or innovations in order to forecast probable consequences. Such mathematical dry runs were possible in some cases before computers, but computers reduced years of computation to minutes.

A classic example of computerized simulation appeared in *The Limits to Growth* (1972), the report of the methods and results of an MIT computer simulation of the world problematique, sponsored by the Club of Rome, an international group of scientists, industrialists, and others organized by Italian industrial consultant Aurelio Peccei. The MIT computer team began by choosing five major variables of the world system: population, capital expenditure, natural resources, pollution, and capital investment in agriculture. They then divided those factors into subvariables, such as rates of birth and death. Next they entered quantitative estimates of the degrees of interaction between the factors, such as the effect of pollution on population. The MIT team then ran the model as if all factors would remain the same in the future, whereupon the computer forecast a disastrous collision between population and resources by the end of the century. When the teams simulated a reduction in the rate at which natural resources would be exploited, the computer forecast a disastrous collision between population and a different variable: pollution. According to further trial runs of this model, global disaster can only be avoided if there are severe growth limits imposed jointly on the rates of capital investment, resource exploitation, and food production. Systems scientists acknowledge that a simulation technique such as this is insufficiently advanced to provide absolute predictability. But they believe simulation is worth further development, and that meanwhile these exercises remind us that planning for any complex system requires an uncommon knack of anticipating the unexpected.

In a systems-analysis approach called *decision theory*, various choices of action are weighed in terms of the statistical probability of the outcome and of the assigned utility values of that outcome. The best choice is defined as that which affords the best chance of the best outcome.

Another application of statistical probability involves *information theory*, which deals with information as a form of mathematically improbable order (negative entropy). Information theory was introduced in 1949 in an article of the *Bell System Technical Journal*, titled "The Mathematical Theory of Communication." The author, Bell Telephone Laboratories communications engineer Claude Elwood Shannon (1916–), was working on the question of how faithful a received message is to the original. For that purpose, he devised a method of measuring the amount of "information" (mathematically improbable order) contained in the original message so that he could compare it with the amount of "information" in the message at its destination. He thus devised an approach in which the efficiency of a communication system could be measured by regarding "information" as a physical quantity, the way physicists treat mass and energy. Information theory, as subsequently developed by Shannon in collaboration with mathematician Warren Weaver, deals with the aforementioned units of information called bits. According to the information theory model, there is a *source* of information (for example, a radio announcer) with a *message* (sound) that is *encoded* by electronic equipment into a *signal* (an electromagnetic wave) that is transmitted on a medium called a *communication channel* (airwaves) which has a limited *channel capacity* and on which a signal may be distorted by *noise* (static) and then is picked up by a receiver on which it is *decoded*. The decoding may be facilitated by redundancy in the original message when that message has been distorted or decimated by noise. (Redundancy in the English language can be illustrated by the fact that *mst ppl hv lttl dffclty in rdng ths sntnc* or similar messages on personalized license plates.) This model of the information process has been widely adopted by communications engineers as a way of uncovering mathematical laws governing informational systems in order to evaluate present information systems and to conceive of information systems of the future. Because information theory offers insights into the phenomenon of communication in general, and because it views information as a measure of order or negative entropy in general, it has been the subject of several attempts to apply it to systems questions in biology, psychology, linguistics, and the social sciences. But information theory success in those areas has been a matter of dispute. As Bertalanffy noted: "Information theory has been hailed as a major [general systems] breakthrough, but outside the original technological field, contributions have remained scarce."

Information theory is sometimes used in combination with *queuing theory*, a mathematical procedure to minimize waiting in systems that tend to get jammed by crowding, such as airports, telephone networks, and data banks. Queuing theory may be applied to information theory when the channels in an information system become overcrowded.

A mathematical approach to maximizing opportunities for

success in competition and conflict is called *game theory.* This approach draws on the analogy between strategy in parlor games (chess, poker, etc.) and strategy in economic, political, and military conflict. Game theory was introduced in a scientific paper of 1928 by Budapest-born mathematician and quantum-physics pioneer John von Neumann (1903–1972), who spent the 1930s onward at the Institute for Advanced Study in Princeton. During World War Two, the American physicist Philip Morse applied game theory to the analysis of submarine warfare. Shortly before the end of the war, in 1944, von Neumann and German-American economist Oskar Morgenstern showed how game theory could be adapted to peaceful competition in their book, *Theory of Games and Economic Behavior.* According to game theory, mathematics can be used for identifying options and outcomes of those options so as to maximize the "game player's" gains and minimize his losses in any system of rational conflict. Because the theory applies only to conflicts in which the adversaries are pursuing their self interest by rational means, it failed to win any enthusiasm from Bertalanffy.

> If game theory is applied to actual political or military situations, the unrealistic character of this assumption becomes immediately apparant. Anybody who has lived through the early decades of this century knows from experience how irrational human behavior is.

Bertalanffy granted, however, that "the theory may provide explanations in principle for psychological and social phenomena." Indeed, game theory literature has produced some useful mental tools to help us think about conflict situations. For example, game theory strategists remind us that the first step in preparing for any real-life conflict is to pay attention to the question of whether the game is one of *perfect information,* in which each adversary knows the whole situation (as in chess) or is a game of *imperfect information* (like poker), in which each adversary knows his own "hand" but not the "hand" of his opponent. Too often, Bertalanffy advised his students, people enter into conflicts without giving sufficient thought to the problems inherent in a game of imperfect information. He went on to advise that a much more common and serious mistake is for people to assume that all adversary situations are what game-theory strategists call *zero-sum games,* in which anything "A" wins must result in an equal loss for "B," so that the sum of the gains and losses add up to zero. The fact is that many real-life competitions are *non-zero-sum games,* and we ignore that fact at our peril. Two examples are the Cold War, in which both sides could win if there is genuine peace or lose if there is all-out war, and the global scramble for natural resources, in which all sides could win if there is dedicated cooperation or lose if the world continues with its wasteful competition.

The frontier of mathematical systems theory includes two approaches that emerged in the 1960s: *fuzzy set theory* and *catastrophe theory*.

Fuzzy set theory, or *fuzzy set logic,* is a technique designed to enable computers to deal with systems involving fuzzy (imprecise) sets of categories such as tall/short. In classical logic, a category either fits or it does not: a person is either tall or he isn't. But such designations are fuzzy in real life. As developed by University of California at Berkeley electrical engineer Lotfi Zadeh, fuzzy set logic assigns each fuzzy quality in a system a numerical spectrum that ranges from "0" to "1". For example, the "0" of tallness would be assigned to Mickey Rooney, and the "1" would be awarded to Kareem Abdul-Jabbar. Persons in between would receive ratings such as "0.1," "0.2," and so on. According to a 1979 report in the *International Journal of General Systems,* fuzzy sets are beginning to play a significant role in general systems research, especially in the study of industrial systems, where human performance sometimes must be measured according to imprecise catagories. An article in the *New Scientist* of May 6, 1982, reports that fuzzy logic not only enables researchers to model systems that would otherwise be too complex, it also makes the computer's "perception" of a problem more like the perception of a human.

Catastrophe theory, developed by French mathematician René Thom, picks up where calculus leaves off. Whereas calculus applies mathematical analysis to continuous events, such as the flow of cars on a highway, catastrophe theory applies mathematical analysis to patterns of discontinuous events, such as highway accidents. According to catastrophe theory, there are mathematical laws for all discontinuous events (abrupt changes or "catastrophes"); therefore, future development of catastrophe theory may lead to the discovery of these laws and consequently to the scientific prediction of abrupt changes of systems in general. A general-systems catastrophe law, for example, would apply to the collapse of bridges or marriages, the explosion of volcanoes or psychotics, or the booms and busts of national economies. Catastrophe-theory researchers deal with the concept of catastrophe (discontinuous events) as a sudden rise or fall on a graph, marking an abrupt change in the quantity under consideration. Catastrophe-theory researchers in England, according to *Science Digest*, have been studying the behavior of prison inmates in order to devise a graph model that might be used to forecast the likelihood of riots.

Cybernetics and GST

The most widely known mathematical systems approach is *cybernetics*, a study of systems in terms of communication and control. The term *cybernetics* has grown extremely elastic with fashionable use, so that it is now often equated with the broad fields of information processing and computer science. But its core concern is the mechanical and physiological phenomenon of self-regulation, as demonstrated by thermostats, endocrine systems, automatic pilots, and guided missiles. The conceptual model of cybernetics is the *feedback loop*, in which the system maintains a steady state or moves toward a certain goal by continually correcting itself as a result of monitoring a feedback of information about its own performance.

The self-correcting process in the thermostat model is called a *negative feedback loop* because the information is used to negate change. A feedback mechanism can also operate as a *positive feedback loop* by continually reinforcing a particular change, as when the stock market spirals up or down in self-fulfilling reaction to its own moods or when a child's behavior steadily improves with praise or deteriorates with blame. Undesirable positive feedback loops—such as unemployment that reduces purchasing power that causes more unemployment, or inflation that causes panic-buying that causes more inflation—are better known as vicious circles. The feedback concept can help put certain systems problems in perspective: a complex problem sometimes can be seen more clearly if it can be defined in terms of reversing a feedback loop from positive to negative or vice versa, or of repairing the communication function of the loop so that the system will react to information that is accurate. Feedback loops that feed back misinformation—as in careless journalism, or myopic diplomacy—can be the undoing of otherwise viable systems.

Cybernetics was developed by MIT mathematician Norbert Wiener (1894–1964). Wiener had achieved international renown in many areas of mathematics by the time he accepted a World War Two assignment to work on the problem of gunfire control (pointing a gun to fire at a moving target). His work on that project prompted him to contribute innovations in control-and-communications engineering, which in turn led to his famous 1948 book, *Cybernetics* (from the Greek word for steersman, *kubērnētes*), subtitled *Control and Communication in the Animal and the Machine.* Wiener spent much of the rest of his life promoting the interdisciplinary versatility of the cybernetic model of self-correcting feedback. He said that the same feedback principle that guides *servomechanisms*—automatic devices that control machines by monitoring their output—can also be used to understand how living organisms like ourselves use informational feedback for guidance in walking, riding a bike, or driving a car, and also how feedback relates to communication and control in psychology and sociology.

In a *Cybernetics* sequel addressed to lay readers, *The Human Use of Human Beings: Cybernetics and Society*, Wiener declared that "society can only be understood through the study of the messages and communication facilities which belong to it." He acknowledged that there are differences in messages and in problems of control, not only between a living organism and a machine, but also within each of those categories. But he declared that, while taking such differences into account, cybernetics should develop techniques to attack the problem of control and communication in general.

Wiener's quest for general cybernetic principles was understandably appealing to some scientists who were committed to the study of systems in general. And there is no denying that every model of a feedback loop is a model of a system in action, a model of the general systems concept of self-regulation. Not surprisingly, then, one of the most prominent members of the systems movement, English biologist W. Ross Ashby (1903–1972), became an apostle of cybernetics. Ashby, the author of *Design for a Brain* (1952) and *Introduction to Cybernetics* (1956), aligned himself with the mechanistic wing of the systems movement by advancing the view that the human brain was just a system of mechanical components, not essentially different from a sophisticated machine.

In contrast with Ashby and others in the systems movement, Bertalanffy damned cybernetics with faint praise, and occasionally he just damned it. His attitude on this subject may have been partly personal: cybernetics upstaged other areas of systems thought to such an extent that many writers began assuming cybernetics was synonymous with GST. As a result, Bertalanffy often felt called upon to recall that he had pioneered systems thinking two decades before cybernetics exploded on the conceptual horizon. However,

Bertalanffy's attitude also reflected a profound philosophic opposition:

> Cybernetics proved its impact in technology. But it did not provide a worldview, being an extension rather than a replacement of the mechanistic view and machine theory. . . . The concept appeals to a time when control engineering and automation are flourishing; computers, servomechanisms, etc., are in the center of interest, and the model of "the organism as servomechanism" appeals to the *Zeitgeist* of a mechanized society. Thus the feedback concept sometimes [eclipses] equally necessary and fruitful viewpoints.

Bertalanffy emphasized that the cybernetic model is a limited view of a system. He regarded it as merely "a subclass of general systems" in the sense that it concentrated on feedback to the exclusion of other systems phenomena. And he described it as *inherently* mechanistic, in the sense that the feedback model (like the homeostasis model) was really "the stimulus-response model of behavior with the addition of a feedback loop." Bertalanffian general systems theory acknowledges the feedback principle in the form of homeostasis, Bertalanffy noted, but his GST focused on the full range of systems phenomena, including open-systems spontaneity, equifinality, and anamorphosis. For Bertalanffy, the value of cybernetics was pretty much limited to its use as a theory of control-mechanisms in technology.

A New Frankenstein Monster?

Bertalanffy's overall feelings about systems technocracy sometimes resembled the paternal ambivalence of Dr. Frankenstein. On some occasions, Bertalanffy declared that the widespread practice of systems engineering and systems analysis demonstrated that the systems concept had practical value: "Thus [I] was vindicated [in being] among the first to predict that the concept of system is to become a fulcrum in modern scientific thought." On other occasions, he deplored the use of systems engineering and systems analysis on behalf of mechanistic goals. He thus echoed the humanistic concern of philosopher George Santayana: "What irony there would be in having learned to control matter, if we thereby forget the purpose of the soul in controlling it."

Though Bertalanffy had devoted decades to the promotion of the systems approach as an alternative to mechanism, he found himself in the position of warning that the systems approach had in part become mechanism's accomplice. He must have experienced more than a little discomfort when he wrote: "Systems science, centered in computer technology, cybernetics, automation, and systems engineering, appears to make the systems idea another—and indeed the ultimate—technique to shape man and society ever more into the 'Megamachine' which [social critic Lewis] Mumford has so impressively described in its advance through history."

The paradox of a systems pioneer issuing a warning about systems science was explained by GST psychiatrist William Gray in the Bertalanffy *Festschrift*:

> There is a basic and profound difference between mechanistic, or pragmatic, systems theory on the one hand and [Bertalanffy's humanistic-organismic systems theory] on the other. The former has developed in response to the burgeoning needs of science and technology and has done so in a fashion that is indeterminate of human values and goals. [Bertalanffy's] systems theory, on the other hand . . . has from the start been humanistic in focus, centering its attention on living systems, on the characteristics of the human being as a complex, living system, and on the systems characteristics of man's symbolic creations, his social systems, culture, psychology, science, technology,

religion, and art. . . . In a world where systems theory threatens to mechanize man and to frustrate his aspiration for individuality, [Bertalanffy's GST] offers the profound hope of [reintroducing] the human element which was lost.

Two scathing attacks on mechanistic systems science were published in the 1960s, and Bertalanffy straightaway began recommending them to his classes and lecture audiences. One was anthropologist Jules Henry's *Culture Against Man* (1963), a wide-ranging denunciation of the scientific establishment. The second was *The New Utopians* (1965), by a systems-science insider, Robert Boguslaw, a senior social scientist at the prestigious System Development Corporation. Boguslaw censured his own profession for stressing efficiency at the expense of human values:

Perhaps the most notable difference to be found between classical utopians [like Thomas More, Charles Fourier, and Francis Bacon] and their contemporary counterparts [systems engineers, systems analysts, etc.] consists precisely in the fact that the humanitarian bent has disappeared. The dominant value orientation of systems technocrats can best be described as "efficiency" rather than "humanitarianism."

Boguslaw's phrase, *New Utopians*, was adopted by Bertalanffy to identify zealous systems practitioners—"the terrible systematizers," as Theodore Roszak dubbed them a few years later—who seemed determined to design people for systems rather than vice versa.

Bertalanffy voiced his opposition to mechanistic systems science at the 1967 annual meeting of the American Psychiatric Association:

Systems designers, analysts, researchers, behavioral engineers, and members of similar professions—New Utopians, as Boguslaw called them—contribute to or even lord over the industrial-military establishment. Elaborating weapons systems, dominating advertising and mass media, and in general preparing a cybernetic society of the future, they must of necessity tend to exclude or suppress the human element. For this human element—individualistic, capricious, often unforeseeable—is precisely the unreliable part of the Megamachine of the present and future. Hence, [the New Utopians feel the human element] should be either replaced by computers and other hardware or else made "reliable"—that is, as machinelike, automated, uniform, conformist, and controlled as possible.

Bertalanffy's criticism from within the systems movement—his indictment of what he called "the darker aspects of this development"—did not become widely known. Consequently, ignorance and misunderstanding about Bertalanffy's thought have generated predictably unfounded criticism. Four years after Bertalanffy's death, such criticism congealed into ridicule in a book-length essay by author David Berlinsky, *On Systems Analysis*. Most of that volume was an accusation of guilt by association, in which Bertalanffy was directly and indirectly blamed for the excesses of systems cultism and quackery that Bertalanffy had specifically denounced. Berlinsky associated Bertalanffy with a "zoo" of systems pseudo-scientists by referring to Bertalanffy as the zoo "master," and by implying that Bertalanffy was more or less responsible for the conflicting views and speculations that appeared over the years in the SGSR yearbooks and other systems literature. Zeroing in on Bertalanffy himself, Berlinsky showed no awareness that Bertalanffy had emphatically distinguished general systems theory from other systems approaches: "General system theory is nothing if not ambitious. In the opening chapter of his text, *General System Theory*, Professor von Bertalanffy claims information theory . . . game theory, decision theory, the theory of automata, and cybernetics as parts of GST." In the same snide manner, Berlinsky referred to those various systems approaches as "affable disciplines," because of their "promiscuous identification with GST." He then issued a blanket accusation that Bertalanffy and everyone else in the systems "zoo" were advocates of a narrow-minded perspective of systems mechanism.

A more informed but nevertheless flawed criticism of Bertalanffy appeared in *Systems Analysis in Public Policy: A Critique* (1972), by Ida R. Hoos, a research sociologist at UC Berkeley. Hoos conceded that "Bertalanffy tempered his endorsement of the systems approach by a few thoughtful caveats" about "incautious expansion to fields for which its concepts are not made," "distortions of reality through 'forcible imposition' of mathematical models," and the use of pseudo-scientific "vague analogies." She also quoted Bertalanffy as warning that systems zealots could "hasten the process of mechanization, automation, and the devaluation of man." But, oddly, she went on to reproach him for failing to prevent the sins committed in the name of systems analysis. She declared that Bertalanffy's warnings had been "too general to serve as useful guidelines and too weak to [dampen] enthusiasm for applying quantitative methods about the quality of human life." At least one of Bertalanffy's warnings must have gotten by Hoos entirely: she accused him of embracing the conceptual model of cybernetic feedback and of advocating cybernetic approaches to biology, psychology and sociology.

The mistake of equating Bertalanffian GST with systems technocracy has also occurred in the Soviet Union, judging from a 1960 article in the journal *Voprosy Filosofii* (translated by Anatol Rapoport for the *General Systems* yearbook):

> The classical works of dialectical materialism have a very great significance for the investigation of methodological principles of systems. Written long before Bertalanffy's, the works of K. Marx (*Capital, Critique of Political Economy*, and others), of F. Engels (*Anti-Duhring, Dialectics of Nature)*, and of V. I. Lenin (*Materialism and Empirio-criticism, Philosophic Notebooks*) contain very rich material on the methodology of sys-

tems research. As far as the development of methodological principles of systems analysis is concerned, the works of Bertalanffy contain in primitive form what had been formulated precisely and analyzed in detail by the classical writers of dialectical materialism fifty to seventy-five years ago.

In one respect, much of the inaccurate criticism of Bertalanffy must be at least partially excused. There might have been less of it, and there might have been more of the recognition he deserved as the father of *humanistic* general systems theory, if this interdisciplinary genius had disciplined himself long enough to sit down and systematize all his important concepts in one book.

At any rate, Bertalanffy's thoughts about the systems movement seem well worth recalling today:

> Any science presents a Janus-face of possibly beneficial and menacing consequences . . . and certainly the systems approach can be used for the further mechanization and enslavement of man. But this is part of the ambivalence of every science. Whether we envisage the positive expansion of knowledge and the beneficient control of the environment and society, or see in the systems movement the arrival of *Brave New World* and *1984*, it deserves intensive study. We have to come to terms with it.

The world of systems technocracy—in the U.S., the U.S.S.R., and elsewhere—did not need Bertalanffy to bring it into being. Likewise, today, the world of systems technocracy does not need any posthumous guidance from him about how to enhance its awesome technical skills. But it seems to the present writer that the systems technocrats and all the rest of us are very much in need of Bertalanffy's humanistic general systems theory, to help us think more clearly about the survival of the human species and the nurturing of the human spirit.

9

Systems Epistemology:
THE MANY FLAVORS OF TRUTH

Universe lies on top of universe, layer after layer, distinct and separate, like a Neapolitan ice [cream cake]. What's true in the chocolate layer, at the bottom, doesn't hold in the vanilla at the top. And a lemon truth is different from a strawberry truth. And each one has just as much right to exist and to call itself real as every other.

Aldous Huxley, *Those Barren Leaves*

Aldous Huxley's metaphor about the many flavors of truth was Bertalanffy's favorite literary reference to epistemology, the study of the nature and validity of human knowledge. Bertalanffy regarded the Huxley image as a vivid way to illustrate Bertalanffy's *perspectivism*: the viewpoint that the validity of knowledge depends on the perspective from which that knowledge is perceived.

To illustrate his perspectivism, Bertalanffy cited various possible perspectives of a table: "The same table is to the physicist an aggregate of electrons, protons, and neutrons; to the chemist a composition of certain organic compounds; to the biologist, a complex of wood cells; to the art historian, a baroque object; to the economist, a utility of certain monetary value, etc." Obviously, said Bertalanffy, all those views are valid and none is more authentic than the other. Less obviously, he emphasized, there is equal justification for the worldviews of science, the arts, and metaphysics.

Bertalanffy's perspectivism, a logical extension of the GST generalist approach to knowledge, was presented by him as an alternative to the extremes of nihilism and absolutism.

In contrast to nihilism, which proclaims that a world without absolute truth is a world without meaning and therefore not worthy of our effort, Bertalanffy's perspectivism pictured a world rich with the truth of many perspectives.

In contrast to absolutism, Bertalanffy's perspectivism endorsed the Socratic maxim that the learned person is someone who is aware of his ignorance. That humility, said Bertalanffy, is not only attractive but quite necessary because anyone who believes he has discovered absolute truth will tend to close his mind to valuable new ideas. Moreover, Bertalanffy warned, the human experience is bloodstained with the horrors perpetrated by true believers, such as those of the Inquisition, the Reign of Terror, the Third Reich, and numerous recent examples of ignorance in action.

Bertalanffy was particularly concerned about epistemological absolutism in science, the *scientism* that assigns value to nothing but science itself. He believed scientism could be as dangerous as the fanaticism of religion or politics, to the extent that scientistic dogma is used to justify the construction of a society of beehive efficiency. He warned about the influence of scientism in American education, industry, and government. And, in the margins of a book he was reading a few days before his death—Columbia University science historian Loren R. Graham's *Science and Philosophy in the Soviet Union* (1972)—he scribbled his opposition to the Marxist view that the ultimate reality is matter: "Dialectical materialism . . . may lead to gross or naive materialism—[the belief that] ultimate reality is governed by physical principles [despite the fact that] the latter are only models produced by the limited human mind."

His note about "gross or naive materialism" echoed published comments of his in which he had argued that the search for general systems laws did not imply "a bleak materialism, a soulless and godless nature." Nothing that scientists do, he declared, can ever invalidate the effort of those who seek reality by means of metaphysical intuition. Paraphrasing Michelangelo's statement that "the true work of art is but a shadow of divine perfection," he said the work of science "is but a humble way to redraw a few traces of the great blueprint of Creation."

Bertalanffy believed that pure reason has its limits—as indicated by questions for which rational answers appear to be beyond our grasp: Does the universe have a limit in space and time? Was there a First Cause? Can a being with infinite power create a rock too heavy for that being to lift? Can a person be telling the truth when he says he always lies?

As a person who apparently used his brain to the utmost, Bertalanffy was intimately aware of the limits of human powers of cognition. Likewise, he wrote, scientists must be aware that "perception is not a reflection of 'real things' [but rather] is an interaction between knower and known." Thus, the observer and the subject of observation interact as a system. The observer cannot observe "real things" because the act of observation has an effect on the entity being observed, whether the entity is an electron or an election. The results of every scientific investigation and every public opinion poll are partly the result of the viewpoint and methodology of the person or persons responsible for the effort.

Acknowledgement of the interaction between knower and known was the basis of what Bertalanffy called his *systems epistemology*, the belief that all seemingly objective perceptions of reality are filtered through the lenses of our biological and psychocultural nature:

> No worldview, general systems theory included, is ultimate truth or ultimate reality. Each is a perspective or an aspect, with all-too-human limitations owing to man's natural and cultural bondage. We cannot jump over our own shadow. General systems theory,

therefore is perspectivistic, not a "nothing-but" philosophy but a view that is tolerant of other philosophies and experiences.

Bertalanffy held that humans create their own reality, not because objective reality doesn't exist but because human knowledge depends on what humans are able and willing to perceive. In a course he taught on perspectivism, he explained:

> There are no facts flying around in nature as if they are butterflies that you put into a nice orderly collection. Our cognition is not a mirroring of ultimate reality but rather is an active process, in which we create models of the world. These models direct what we actually see, what we consider as fact.

His definition of an observed fact was: "a certain aspect isolated from the stream of experience for certain intellectual pursuits." All facts observed by scientists, therefore, are images of reality that have been selected for the purpose of scientific theory or technology.

His perspectivistic view also extended to the assumptions woven into accounts of history:

> In a certain sense, every historical interpretation is a falsification. There is no completely objective political history, and the same holds for the history of science and philosophy. The mere fact of selection out of innumerable recorded data implies the historian's bias, which is the stronger the less he is aware of it.

By the same token, he could have cited the unavoidable bias of selectivity in all forms of education and journalism. If Bertalanffy had watched television, he might have suggested that Walter Cronkite amend his famous sign-off statement by saying, "That's the way it is . . . edited."

In addition to rejecting epistemological absolutism in rela-

214

tion to human experience, Bertalanffy dismissed the *a priori* (independent-of-experience) view of reality advanced by the founder of German philosophic idealism, Immanuel Kant (1724–1804). The Kantian epistemology was based on the assumption that we are born with absolute categories of thinking, innate mental patterns that determine our ideas about space, time, and so forth. Furthermore, said Kant, these mental categories mirror ultimate reality. Bertalanffy held that Kant's categorical absolutism was disproved by the fact that our categories of thinking tend to change along with changes in our scientific worldview, and by the additional fact that our modern categories of space and time are subject to relativity.

Having rejected epistemological absolutism, however, Bertalanffy did not embrace total relativism, the view that there is no relationship at *all* between knowledge and reality. He said he called his viewpoint perspectivism rather than relativism because he wanted to specify that the various levels of knowledge are valid within their limits. He noted, for example, that flies, dogs, and humans each have their own limited knowledge of the world, but such knowledge must have some validity or else flies, dogs, and humans would not have survived the struggle for existence.

Citing the work in comparative psychology of German biologist Jakob Johann von Uexküll (1864–1944), Bertalanffy observed that "from the great cake of reality, every living organism cuts a slice, which it can perceive and to which it can react owing to its psychophysical organization, that is, the structure of receptor [sensory] and effector [reactive] organs." Every organism, in Uexküll's terminology, perceives its own *Umwelt* (environment). For instance, our world is three-dimensional, but not so with animals that have their eyes pointing sideways. And our sense of time is partly conditioned by the fact that our eyes can freeze images of action at 1/18th of a second (our "instant" or smallest unit of perceived time), whereas experiments have shown that the visual unit is much longer for a snail and much shorter for the fast-moving Siamese fighting fish.

Moving from the epistemological role of biology to the epistemological role of culture, Bertalanffy noted that a cultural perspective will determine which features of experienced reality are emphasized and which are underplayed. Artists of ancient Egypt, he pointed out, showed kings to be imposingly tall, court officials somewhat smaller and ordinary folk downright diminutive. He might have added that our republic produced a popular comic strip called *The Little King*, and that one of our World War Two heroes, General Douglas MacArthur, was deliberately made to appear taller than he was by army and press photographers.

In the cultural sphere, Bertalanffy commended the hypothesis of American linguist Benjamin Lee Whorf (1897–1941). According to Whorf, a person's worldview is largely determined by assumptions that are implicit in that person's native language. As an example, Whorf compared the Hopi language, which makes no distinction of tenses, to Indo-European languages, which emphasize time and therefore tend to produce cultures of clocks and clockwatchers.

Bertalanffy had one criticism of the *Whorfian hypothesis*. He faulted it for not taking into account the fact that the relationship between language and worldview is interactive. Bertalanffy believed that worldviews can fashion language just as much as vice versa. In support of that contention, Bertalanffy cited the impact on language of religious, political, and commercial environments. The Bertalanffy amendment to the Whorfian hypothesis was crucial to Bertalanffy's thought because he believed that humans have a unique evolutionary destiny: "In contrast to the animal, which has an ambient *(Umwelt)* determined by its organization, man himself creates his world, which we call human culture." Bertalanffy allowed that we can be captives of our culture, but he insisted that we didn't *have* to be. As open systems, we are active as well as reactive.

He also related his perspectivism to his concept that humans interact with a whole universe of symbols, including not only language but mathematics, art, and values:

Every symbolic world, science included, is determined by innumerable factors of biological, anthropological, linguistic, and historical nature. Any symbolic system represents a certain facet of reality. None of the worlds of symbols, the sum total of which is human culture, is a full presentation of reality. However, each aspect has [some] truth.

To place Bertalanffy's perspectivism in perspective: he was a scientist who denied that science is *the* truth but who insisted that science is *a* truth. His epistemological defense of science on that level prompted him to scold Uexküll for giving the impression that "the world of physics, from the atoms and electrons to the galaxies, is merely a human product, dependent on the mind-body organization of man." Bertalanffy branded that notion demonstrably false in light of objective evidence—confirming scientific knowledge—from extra-human perceptions of instruments that detect data from such sources as ultraviolet light and x-rays. Bertalanffy made this case for the perspectivistic validity of scientific knowledge:

> Whistler called painting the art of omission, representing things by a few characteristic traces. Something similar is true of science. It is not concerned with the innermost core of reality. But it is one of the perspectives of reality, representing, by means of interconnected symbols, certain traces of reality, namely the orderliness in the relations of things. This, however, is sufficient to allow for theoretical as well as practical mastery of nature.

Bertalanffy held art and mysticism to be equally valid, "not in the way of controlling the world by technical marvels but in the way of self-realization of the human personality." He wrote: "We are not only scientific intellects, we are also human beings. To express in momentous symbols the core of reality, that is what myth, poetry, and philosophy are trying."

And so, there was nothing contradictory about the fact that Bertalanffy's favorite intellectual forebear was a fifteenth-century German mystic, Nicholas Krebs, better known as Cardinal Nicholas of Cusa. Bertalanffy wrote two scholarly studies of Nicholas, in one of which he said: "In his person and thought, the great Cardinal united the mysticism of the vanishing Middle Ages with the rationality of the nascent modern times [the early Renaissance]. Thus, science and enlightenment grew out of the spirit of mysticism."

In Nicholas' philosophy, Bertalanffy saw "the mighty spectacle of the birth of the modern spirit." Justifying such grand words, Bertalanffy pointed out that—though Nicholas pre-dated Copernicus, Kepler, and Galileo—Nicholas advanced the idea that the Earth orbits the sun, that the sun is one of a multitude of stars with their own planets, that other planets are inhabited by intelligent civilizations, and that the universe is infinite. (Infinity at that time was an extremely advanced idea in science and a decidedly dangerous idea in theology; 136 years after Nicholas' death, Nicholas-disciple Giordano Bruno, the Italian philosopher-monk, paid for the offense of preaching Nicholas' cosmological ideas of infinity, etc., by being burned alive by the Inquisition.) Nicholas also conceived the idea that plants draw sustenance from the air, and he suggested that medical diagnosis would be facilitated by the counting of pulse beats. What made these intellectual breakthroughs all the more remarkable was that he arrived at them entirely by intuition.

Bertalanffy had no reluctance about applying Cardinal Nicholas' religious insights to the worldview of general systems theory. Bertalanffy christened Nicholas "a sort of father figure of holism" because Nicholas had proclaimed, *"Ex omnibus partibus relucet totum"* ("From every part, the whole shines forth"). Nicholas' intention in that statement had been to express the idea that God is the universe and that the God-universe is mirrored in every part of the universe. Bertalanffy's interpretation was perspectivistic:

From this point of view, the universe is God's image. Nicholas approves, therefore, the dictum of the Greek philosopher Anaxagoras: 'Everything is in everything'; any part of the world contains, in a limited way, the infinite whole. Any part is, as it were, an organ of the universe, composing with others a complete organism. Reminiscent of Heraclitus: God, as the animating principle of an organismic world, is compared to fire, so that all becoming is due to modifications of fire, or, as we would say today, transformations of energy. This idea, which appears so modern to us, is amplified in the statement that it is number, measure, and weight that hold together the architecture of the universe.

Bertalanffy also adopted Nicholas' concept of *coincidentia oppositorium* (a unity of opposites), as represented by divine reconciliation of good and evil, body and soul, male and female, day and night, existence and non-existence. Bertalanffy regarded *coincidentia oppositorium* as an apt description of the paradoxes of modern science, such as the contradictory but equally useful wave and particle models of the electron.

Considering the admiration that Bertalanffy had for Cardinal Nicholas, perhaps there was more than coincidence to the fact that the subject of Bertalanffy's doctoral dissertation, nineteenth-century physicist Gustav Fechner, also happened to be a mystic. Fechner championed the panentheist view that all entities in the universe are parts of the body of God. That worldview was not necessarily inconsistent with Bertalanffy's GST: "We begin to see the world as a great organization, lawfully ascending from the ultimate particles of physics to living organisms and eventually to man and his supra-individual socio-symbolic systems."

Kenneth Boulding, a member of the Society of Friends, has written that an awareness of the universe as a total system "is an experience which we need not be ashamed to call religious."

In Bertalanffy's role as a scientist, he scrupulously disassociated himself from mysticism, most notably when he offered his organismic biology as a non-vitalistic answer to mechanism. But he was careful to give mysticism its separate-but-equal due. Consider, for example, the following comment: "The scientist can say that *Homo sapiens* is the highest product of terrestial evolution. The mystics say essentially the same when claiming evolution to be God becoming aware of Himself." Bertalanffy thus articulated the idea that science and mysticism are parallel approaches to reality, a view anticipating the science-mysticism dualism given prominence in a 1975 bestseller, *The Tao of Physics*, by a 1966 Ph.D. from the University of Vienna, UC Berkeley physicist Fritjof Capra. Bertalanffy held the opinion, expressed by Capra, that "science does not need mysticism and mysticism does not need science, but man needs both."

Bertalanffy's deepest feelings about life seemed to waver between wonder and despair. Like the agnostic Darwin, Bertalanffy was in awe of the beauty and diversity of the natural world and yet painfully puzzled by nature's apparent cruelty. Bertalanffy once confessed that he could not help wondering about the meaning of an evolutionary drama in which "life spirals laboriously upwards to higher and ever higher levels, paying for every step" with the introduction, at ascending levels, of death, pain, anxiety, and lastly a technologically sophisticated aggression that threatens to bring the whole drama to an end.

Though the meaning of life eluded him, he seemed to believe that a meaning did exist. His life's partner, Maria, explained his private metaphysical outlook to me in these words: "Ludwig did not practice a religion. He did not follow the Bible or what any particular church said. But he did like mysticism. For Ludwig, mysticism was a feeling one has, a feeling of something higher, something beyond this world. Though it's hard for me to express, I can tell you that he did believe in something. I mean, he believed that there *is* something. We often talked about it, because it was a belief we shared. But, of course, Ludwig devoted most of his life to thinking about the world that's right here."

A few months before his death, in a discussion with some of his students, Professor Ludwig von Bertalanffy commented: "I cannot offer a wonder drug or panacea for the salvation of society. I'm not Mister Know-It-All and I cannot promise you answers. But perhaps our discussion will help us a little bit to better understand those pressing problems with which we are confronted. The only thing we can hope for is perhaps getting a little bit wiser about our problems and about what can be done. So let us discuss these things as far as you and I are able to do so—because you see, I want to be of some use to you. If I succeed in making a very tiny contribution in that way, then I would be satisfied."

GLOSSARY

Anamorphosis. In biology, the tendency to evolve toward increasing complexity. Not to be confused with the same word in art, meaning a distorted image that can be seen correctly only from an unusual direction or through a distorting mirror.

Automata theory. A mathematical systems approach that explores the potential of computers by employing a theoretical model of a computer with infinite memory.

Axiology. The study of the nature and criteria of values, usually in the context of ethical systems.

Behaviorism. A school of psychology that regards only quantifiable behavior as a valid focus, to the exclusion of phenomena that other schools ascribe to consciousness and mind.

Boundary definition. The determination of the proper scope for any systems inquiry.

Catastrophe theory. A mathematical systems approach to patterns of discontinuous events.

Classical systems theory. The application of calculus to describe the dynamic behavior of open systems. Also called dynamic systems theory.

Closed system. A system considered to be isolated from its environment.

Computerized simulation. A systems approach in which a mathematical model of a system is fed to a computer and then subjected to hypothetical changes.

Culturology. The study of how cultural systems have behaved through history and how that behavior may reveal patterns that are indicative of cultural systems laws.

Cybernetics. A study of systems in terms of communication and control.

Dynamic morphology. The Bertalanffian view that morphology and physiology (the studies of biological form and function) should be treated as different approaches to the same phenomena.

Egalitarianism. A viewpoint, regarded by Bertalanffy as a distortion of democracy, holding that all individuals are equally capable of every achievement.

Entelechy. A spirit-like force that, according to vitalists, accounts for the inner-directed activity of living organisms.

Entropy. A natural trend toward maximum disorder, prevailing in the inanimate world.

Environmentalism. As described by Bertalanffy, this is a viewpoint that falsely attributes all human traits to the influence of experience, without taking into account the role of innate factors.

Epistemology. The study of the nature and validity of human knowledge.

Equifinality. A fundamental characteristic of open systems, by which the same goal is reached from different starting points and in different ways.

Exponential law. A general systems law of growth or decay at a constant rate.

Field theory. Social psychologist Kurt Lewin's approach to human behavior as a function of the individual's interaction with the environment.

Fuzzy set theory. A mathematical technique to enable computers to deal with systems involving imprecise sets of categories.

Game theory. A mathematical systems approach to maximizing opportunities for success in competition and conflict.

General systems theory (GST). Alternately spelled, by Bertalanffy and others, without the plural "s". As used in this book, GST is a holistic way of thinking based on an awareness of the behavior of systems in general. GST also refers to Bertalanffy's proposed discipline that would seek and apply general systems laws.

Gestalt psychology. A school of thought that pioneered the systems approach to human behavior.

Hierarchical order. A key model of general systems thought, depicting reality as a hierarchical architecture of organized entities.

Holism. Any viewpoint that focuses on the whole as well as the parts, because the whole displays characteristics that are not present in the isolated parts. This is a very useful term that unfortunately has been exploited in recent years by purveyors of questionable healing products and practices.

Holons. Systems in hierarchical order. Arthur Koestler's term for wholes that are also parts of other wholes.

Homeostasis. The living organism's process of self-regulation, as in the regulation of body temperature.

Humanism. An outlook that elevates human values above those of technology, commerce, politics, etc. Though the "Moral Majority" has attempted to equate humanism with godless immorality, the term traditionally has been used to describe a profoundly moral standpoint—either spiritual or secular—emphasizing individual human fulfillment and dignity.

Humanistic general systems theory. Alternate term for Bertalanffian GST, underscoring his belief that systems science should be practiced for purposes of humanism rather than sheer technological efficiency.

Information theory. A systems approach that deals with information as a form of mathematically improbable order or negative entropy.

Linear programming. A mathematical systems method of determining the most efficient allocation of limited resources.

Logical positivism. The view that the only valid knowledge is that which can be empirically tested.

Mechanistic conception. The biological viewpoint that all organisms, including humans, are merely complex machines and that all of life can be explained entirely by the laws of physics and chemistry.

Megamachine. Lewis Mumford's term for the mechanized order of society.

Mind-body problem. The classical philosophic-scientific enigma about the relationship of mind and body.

Morphology. The study of living forms.

Negative entropy (negentropy). The biological drive toward increasing order and complexity.

Neo-Darwinism. The mechanistic view that all evolution can be explained by Darwinian natural selection combined with modern discoveries about genetics. Also known as the Modern Synthesis.

Open system. A system that continuously exchanges matter/energy with its environment. Includes all systems that are alive.

Operant conditioning. The behaviorist technique by which an animal or human is conditioned to behave in a specified manner.

Organismic conception (Organicism). In theoretical biology, an alternative to both mechanism and vitalism. The view that the vital characteristics of life arise from nature's laws of organization.

Organismic/systems psychology. The application of the organismic conception to questions of human behavior.

Paradigm. Historian Thomas Kuhn's term for the cluster of basic assumptions that determines what questions scientists of a given era will ask.

Peace research. The use of systems approaches to study the causes and prevention of war.

Perspectivism. Bertalanffy's epistemological viewpoint, holding that the validity of knowledge depends on the perspective from which that knowledge is perceived.

Principle of emergence. The tendency for unpredictable qualities to emerge from the interaction of the parts within a system.

Principle of reactivity. In Bertalanffy's view, this is the false idea that behavior is entirely a reaction to stimuli, to the exclusion of spontaneity.

Problem. In science, a question raised for inquiry. When scientists express a love for problems, therefore, they are not exhibiting masochism.

Progressive centralization. The tendency, as a system becomes more complex, for certain parts to become dominant.

Progressive differentiation. The tendency, as a system becomes more complex, for parts to become specialized.

Progressive integration. The tendency, as a system becomes more complex, for the parts to become increasingly dependent on the whole.

Progressive mechanization. The tendency, related to progressive differentiation, for parts of a system to be limited to a single function.

Queuing theory. A mathematical procedure for making optimal use of available facilities, to minimize waiting in systems that can get jammed by crowding.

Reductionism. The mechanistic assumption that all biological phenomena can be reduced to explanations of physics and chemistry.

Robotomorphism. The image of *Homo sapiens* as a conditioned-response robot.

Scientism. The viewpoint, as defined and disowned by Bertalanffy, that science, particularly physical science, is the only valid approach to reality.

Social Darwinism. A distortion of Darwin's own beliefs, justifying ruthlessness and greed as supposedly natural expressions of the "survival of the fittest."

Steady state. A basic characteristic of open systems, in which constancy is maintained by a continuous flow of input and output. Bertalanffy used this term as an alternative to *equilibrium*, which implies constancy that is static.

Suboptimization. The failure to examine a sufficiently broad picture of any systems problem.

Symbolic theory of human behavior. The belief, advanced by Bertalanffy and others, that all behavior that is specifically human can be traced to our species' invention of a symbolic world of language, science, art, music, ritual, religion, etc.

System. Any entity maintained by the mutual interaction of its parts.

Systems analysis. Generally synonymous with *operations research*. The interdisciplinary search for more efficient ways of using existing talent and technology to improve a system.

Systems engineering. Similar to and sometimes indistinguishable from *systems analysis*. But this approach is more likely to consider the need for a system's fundamental redesign or its replacement.

Systems management. The application of systems principles to the problems of management, commonly but not exclusively in the realm of private enterprise.

Teleology. The explanation of phenomena by reference to some ultimate end for which a thing or event is produced.

Theoretical model. A conceptual construction—such as the solar-system model of the atom—that simplifies an extremely complex system for the sake of scientific investigation.

Unitary concept of mental illness. Karl Menninger's view of psychopathology as a systems disorder.

Values. Enduring beliefs about desirable goals and behavior.

Vitalism. The theory that organisms are directed from within by a vital force that is beyond the explanation of science.

Zoomorphism. The practice of portraying *Homo sapiens* as just another animal.

SELECTED
BIBLIOGRAPHY

Ackoff, Russell L. *Redesigning the Future: A Systems Approach to Societal Problems*. New York: John Wiley and Sons, 1974.

Allport, Gordon. *Becoming*. New Haven: Yale University Press, 1955.

Arieti, Silvano. *The Will to be Human*. New York: Quadrangle Books, 1972.

Ashby, W. Ross. *Design for a Brain*. New York: John Wiley & Sons, 1952.

Bateson, Gregory. *Steps to an Ecology of Mind*. New York: Ballantine, 1972.

———. *Mind and Nature*. New York: E. P. Dutton, 1979.

Berlinski, David. *On Systems Analysis*. Cambridge: The MIT Press, 1976.

Berrien, F. Kenneth. *General and Social Systems*. New Brunswick: Rutgers University Press, 1968.

Bertalanffy, Ludwig von. *Modern Theories of Development* (1928). New York: Harper Torchbook edition, 1961.

———. *Theoretische Biologie* (1932, 1942). Ann Arbor, Mich.: J. W. Edwards, 1948.

———. *Problems of Life* (1952). New York: Harper Torchbook edition, 1961.

———. *Robots, Men and Minds*. New York: Braziller, 1967.

———. *Organismic Psychology and Systems Theory*. Worcester, Mass.: Clark University Press, 1968.

———. *General System Theory*. New York: Braziller, 1968.

———. *Perspectives on General Systems Theory*. New York: Braziller, 1975

———. *A Systems View of Man*. Boulder, Colo.: Westview Press, 1981.

229

———, and Rapoport, Anatol (ed.), *General Systems*. Yearbooks of the Society for General Systems Research, 1956–72.

Boguslaw, W. *The New Utopians*. Englewood Cliffs: Prentice-Hall, 1965.

Bohm, David. *Wholeness and the Implicate Order*. London: Routledge & Kegan Paul, 1981.

Boulding, Kenneth E. *The Organizational Revolution*. New York: Harper & Row, 1953.

———. *The Image*. Ann Arbor: University of Michigan Press, 1956.

Bronowski, Jacob. *Science and Human Values* (1956). New York: Harper Torchbook edition, 1965.

———. *The Common Sense of Science*. Cambridge: Harvard University Press, 1967.

Buckley, Walter. *Sociology and Modern Systems Theory*. Englewood Cliffs: Prentice-Hall, 1967.

———(ed.). *Modern Systems Research for the Behavioral Scientist*. Chicago: Aldine Publishing Co., 1968.

Cannon, W. B. *The Wisdom of the Body*. New York: W. W. Norton Co., 1932.

Capra, Fritjof. *The Tao of Physics*. Boulder, Colo.: Shambhala Publications, 1976.

———. *The Turning Point*. New York: Simon and Schuster, 1982.

Cassirer, E. *The Philosophy of Symbolic Forms* (3 vols.). New Haven: Yale University Press, 1953, 1955, 1957.

Chacko, George K. *Systems Approach to Public and Private Sector Problems*. New York: North-Holland Publishing Co., 1976.

Chase, Stuart. *The Tyranny of Words*. New York: Harcourt, Brace & World, 1938.

Churchman, C. West. *The Systems Approach*. New York: Dell Publishing Co., 1968.

Commoner, Barry. *Science and Survival*. New York: Viking Press, 1966.

Coombs, Philip H. *The World Educational Crisis: A Systems Analysis*. New York: Oxford University Press, 1968.

Cousins, Norman. *In Place of Folly*. New York: Harper & Brothers, 1961.

Darwin, Charles. *The Origin of Species* (1859). New York: The New American Library, 1958.

———. *The Descent of Man* (1871). Princeton, N.J.: Princeton University Press, 1981.

———. *The Autobiography of Charles Darwin, and Selected Letters*. New York: Dover Publications, 1958.

DeGreene, Kenyon B. (ed.). *Systems Psychology*. New York: McGraw-Hill Book Co., 1970.

Dobshansky, T. *The Biology of Ultimate Concern*. New York: The New American Library, 1967.

Driesch, H. *History and Theory of Vitalism*. London: Macmillan, 1914.

Dubos, René. *So Human an Animal.* New York: Charles Scribner's Sons, 1968.

Easton, David. *A Systems Analysis of Political Life.* New York: John Wiley & Sons, 1965.

Eddington, A. *The Nature of Physics.* Ann Arbor: University of Michigan Press, 1958.

Einstein, Albert. *Out of My Later Years.* New York: The Wisdom Library, 1950.

Frankl, Viktor E. *Man's Search for Meaning.* Boston: Beacon Press, 1959.

Freud, Sigmund. *The Basic Writings of Sigmund Freud.* New York: The Modern Library, 1938.

Fromm, Erich. *The Revolution of Hope: Toward a Humanized Technology.* New York: Harper & Row, 1968.

Fuller, R. Buckminster. *Operating Manual for Spaceship Earth.* Carbondale, Ill.: Southern Illinois University Press, 1969.

————. *Synergetics.* New York: Macmillan, 1975.

Galdston, Iago (ed.). *The Interface Between Psychiatry and Anthropology.* New York: Brunner/Mazel, 1971.

Gelwick, Richard. *The Way of Discovery: An Introduction to the Thought of Michael Polanyi.* New York: Oxford University Press, 1977.

Gould, Stephen Jay. *The Mismeasure of Man.* New York: W. W. Norton & Co., 1981.

Graham, Loren R. *Science and Philosophy in the Soviet Union.* New York: Alfred A. Knopf, 1972.

Gray, William, and Duhl, F.D., (eds.). *General System Theory and Psychiatry.* Boston: Little, Brown & Company, 1968.

Gray, William, and Rizzo, Nicholas D. (eds.). *Unity Through Diversity: A Festschrift in Honor of Ludwig von Bertalanffy.* New York: Gordon and Breach, 1973.

Grinker, R. R. (ed.). *Toward a Unified Theory of Human Behavior.* New York: Basic Books, 1956.

Gross, Martin L. *The Psychological Society.* New York: Random House, 1978.

Handler, Philip (ed.). *Biology and the Future of Man.* New York: Oxford University Press, 1970.

Hardin, Garrett, and Balen, John. *Managing the Commons.* New York: W. H. Freeman, 1970.

Heisenberg, W. *Physics and Philosophy: The Revolution of Modern Science.* New York: Harper and Brothers, 1958.

Henry, J. *Culture Against Man.* New York: Random House, 1963.

Hitching, Francis. *The Neck of the Giraffe: Where Darwin Went Wrong.* Boston: Houghton Mifflin Co. 1982.

Hoos, Ida R. *Systems Analysis in Public Policy.* Berkeley: University of California Press, 1972.

Huxley, Aldous. *Brave New World*. New York: Harper and Brother, 1932.

Huxley, Julian. *Evolution in Action*. New York: Harper, 1953.

Katz, D., and Kahn, R. L. *The Social Psychology of Organizations*. New York: John Wiley & Sons, 1966.

Kennedy, John F. *The Burden and the Glory*. New York: Harper & Row, 1964.

Klir, George J. *An Approach to General Systems Theory*. Princeton: Van Norstrand Reinhold Co., 1969.

———(ed.). *Trends in General Systems Theory*. New York: John Wiley & Sons, 1971.

Koestler, Arthur. *The Act of Creation*. New York: The Macmillan Company, 1964.

———. *The Ghost in the Machine*. New York: The Macmillan Company, 1967.

———, and Smythies, J. R. (eds.). *Beyond Reductionism: New Perspectives in the Life Sciences* (Alpbach Symposium of 1968). New York: Macmillan, 1969.

Kohler, Wolfgang. *Gestalt Psychology*. New York: Liveright Publishing Corporation, 1947.

Krone, Robert M. *Systems Analysis and Policy Sciences*. New York: John Wiley & Sons, 1980.

Kuhn, Thomas. *The Structure of Scientific Revolutions*. Chicago: University of Chicago Press, 1962.

Langer, S. K. *Philosophy in a New Key* (1942). New York: Mentor Books, 1948.

———. *Philosophical Sketches*. Baltimore: The Johns Hopkins Press, 1962.

Laszlo, Ervin (ed.). *The Relevance of General Systems Theory: Papers Presented to Ludwig von Bertalanffy on His 70th Birthday*. New York: Braziller, 1972.

———. *The Systems View of the World*. New York: Braziller, 1972.

———. *A Strategy for the Future: The Systems Approach to World Order*. New York: Braziller, 1974.

———, and Wilbur, J. B (eds.). *Human Values and the Mind of Man*. New York: Gordon & Breach, 1971.

Lévi-Strauss, Claude. *Structural Anthropology*. New York: Basic Books, 1963.

Lewin, Kurt. *Field Theory in Social Science*. New York: Harper 1951.

London, Perry. *Behavior Control*. New York: Harper & Row, 1969.

Lorenz, Konrad. *On Aggression*. New York: Harcourt, Brace and World, 1963.

Lotka, Alfred James. *Elements of Physical Biology*. Baltimore: Williams and Wilkins Co., 1925.

Marmor, Judd. *Psychiatry in Transition*. New York: Brunner/Mazel, 1974.

Maslow, Abraham H. *Toward a Psychology of Being*. New York: Van Nostrand, 1968.

Matson, Floyd. *The Broken Image*. New York: Braziller, 1964.

McGinniss, Joe. *The Selling of the President 1968.* New York: Trident Press, 1969.

Meadows, D., *et al. The Limits to Growth.* New York: Universe Books, 1972.

Menninger, Karl, (eds.), with Mayman, M. and Pruyser, P. *The Vital Balance.* New York: Viking Press, 1963.

Mesarovic, Mihajlo D. (ed.). *Views of General Systems Theory.* New York: John Wiley & Sons. 1964.

————, and Yasuhiko Takahara. *General Systems Theory: Mathematical Foundations.* New York: Academic Press, 1975.

Miller, James Grier. *Living Systems.* New York: McGraw Hill, 1978.

Mills, C. Wright. *The Causes of World War Three.* New York: Ballantine Books, Inc., 1958.

Monod, Jacques. *Chance and Necessity.* New York: Alfred A. Knopf, 1971.

Montagu, M. F. Ashley (ed.). *Man and Aggression.* New York: Oxford University Press, 1968.

Morris, Desmond. *The Naked Ape.* New York: McGraw Hill, 1967.

Muller, Herbert J. *Freedom in the Modern World.* New York: Harper & Row, 1966.

Mumford, L. *The Myth of the Machine.* New York: Harcourt, Brace and World, 1967.

Needham, Joseph S. *Order and Life.* New Haven: Yale University Press, 1936.

Neumann, John von, and Morgenstern, O. *Theory of Games and Economic Behavior.* Princeton: Princeton University Press, 1947.

Odum, Howard T. *Environment, Power and Society.* New York: Wiley-Interscience, 1971.

Orwell, George. *1984.* New York: Signet, 1949.

Packard, Vance. *The Hidden Persuaders.* New York: David McKay Company, Inc., 1957.

————. *The People Shapers.* Boston: Little, Brown & Company, 1977.

Parsons, Talcott. *The Social System.* New York: Free Press, 1957.

Pattee, Howard H. (ed.). *Hierarchy Theory: The Challenge of Complex Systems.* New York: Braziller, 1973.

Piaget, Jean. *The Construction of Reality in the Child.* New York: Basic Books, 1959.

Polanyi, Michael. *Personal Knowledge: Towards a Post-Critical Philosophy.* Chicago: University of Chicago Press, 1958.

Popper, Karl R. *The Logic of Scientific Discovery* (1934). New York: Harper, 1959.

Prigogine, I. *Introduction to Thermodynamics of Irreversible Processes.* New York: Wiley-Interscience, 1961.

Ramo, Simon. *Cure for Chaos: Fresh Solutions to Social Problems Through the Systems Approach.* New York: David McKay Company, 1969.

Rapoport, Anatol. *Science and the Goals of Man: A Study in Semantic Orientation.* New York: Harper, 1950.

————. *The Big Two: Soviet-American Perceptions of Foreign Policy.* New York: Pegasus/Bobbs Merrill Co., 1971.

————. (ed.). *Game Theory as a Theory of Conflict Resolution.* Boston: D. Reidel Publishing Co., 1974.

Reich, C. A. *The Greening of America.* New York: Random House, 1971.

Reichenbach, Hans. *The Rise of Scientific Philosophy.* Berkeley: University of California Press, 1951.

Reisman, Arnold. *Systems Analysis in Health-Care Delivery.* Lexington, Mass.: D. C. Heath and Company, 1979.

Reisman, D. *The Lonely Crowd.* New Haven: Yale University Press, 1950.

Rifkin, Jeremy, with Howard, Ted. *Entropy: A New World View.* New York: The Viking Press, 1980.

Rosen, Robert. *Dynamical System Theory in Biology.* New York: John Wiley & Sons, 1970.

Roszak, Theodore. *The Making of a Counter Culture.* New York: Garden City, N.Y.: Doubleday, 1969.

Royce, Joseph R. *The Encapsulated Man.* Princeton: D. Van Nostrand Co., 1964.

————. (ed.). *Psychology and the Symbol.* New York: Random House, 1965.

————, and Leendert, P. Mos (eds.). *Humanistic Psychology.* New York: Plenum Press, 1981.

Rubin, M. D. (ed.). *Man in Systems.* New York: Gordon & Breach, 1971.

Schrödinger, Erwin. *What is Life?* Cambridge: Cambridge University Press, 1945.

Shannon, C. E., and Weaver, W. *The Mathematical Theory of Communication.* Urbana: University of Illinois Press, 1949.

Shapley, Harlow. *Of Stars and Men.* Boston: Beacon Press, 1958.

Sheldrake, Rupert. *A New Science of Life.* Los Angeles: J. P. Tarcher, Inc., 1982.

Simon, Herbert A. *Models of Man.* New York: John Wiley & Sons, 1957.

————. *The Sciences of the Artificial.* Cambridge: The M.I.T. Press, 1969.

Simonton, O. Carl, Matthews-Simon, Stephanie, and Creighton, James. *Getting Well Again.* Los Angeles: J. P. Tarcher, Inc., 1978.

Sinnott, Edmund W. *Cell and Psyche.* Chapel Hill: University of North Carolina, 1950.

————. *The Problem of Organic Form.* New Haven: Yale University Press, 1963.

Skinner, B. F. *Beyond Freedom and Dignity.* New York: Alfred A. Knopf, 1971.

Smuts, Jan Christiaan. *Holism and Evolution.* New York: The Viking Press, 1926.

Sorokin, P.A. *Sociological Theories of Today.* New York: Harper & Row, 1966.

Spengler, Oswald. *Decline of the West.* New York: Alfred A. Knopf, 1939.

Bibliography

St-Germain, Michel. *Etude Synoptique de la Théorie Organismique, de la Théorie des Systèmes Ouverts, de la Théorie Générale des Systèmes de Ludwig von Bertalanffy.* Unpublished doctoral thesis. Ottawa: University of Ottawa, 1979.

Sutherland, John W. *A General Systems Philosophy for the Social and Behavioral Sciences.* New York: George Braziller, 1973.

Szent-Gyorgyi, Albert. *The Crazy Ape.* New York: Philosophical Library, 1970.

Teilhard de Chardin, P. *The Phenomenon of Man.* New York: Harper & Bros., 1959.

Thompson, D'Arcy Wentworth. *On Growth and Form* (1942). Cambridge: Cambridge University Press, 1961.

Toffler, Alvin. *The Third Wave.* New York: William Morrow & Company, 1980.

Toynbee, Arnold. *Change and Habit: The Challenge of Our Time.* New York: Oxford University Press, 1966.

Vico, G. *The New Science* (1744). New York: Doubleday, 1961.

Waddington, C. H. *Tools for Thought.* New York: Basic Books, 1971.

Watson, J. B. *Behaviorism* (1924). Chicago: University of Chicago Press, 1959.

Watt, Kenneth E. F. *Systems Analysis in Ecology.* New York: Academic Press, 1966.

Weinberg, Gerald M. *An Introduction to General Systems Thinking.* New York: John Wiley & Sons, 1975.

————, and Weinberg, Daniela. *On the Design of Stable Systems.* New York: Wiley, 1979.

Weiss, Paul A. (ed.). *Hierarchically Organized Systems in Theory and Practice.* New York: Hafner, 1971.

White, Leslie A. *The Science of Culture.* New York: Grove Press, 1949.

Whitehead, Alfred North. *Science and the Modern World.* New York: The Macmillan Company, 1925.

Whorf, Benjamin Lee. *Language, Thought and Reality.* New York: John Wiley & Sons, 1956.

Whyte, Lancelot Law. *The Next Development in Man.* New York: Mentor Books, 1950.

————. Wilson, Albert G. and Wilson, Donna (eds.). *Hierarchical Structures.* New York: American Elsevier Publishing Co., 1969.

Whyte, William H., Jr. *The Organization Man.* New York: Simon & Schuster, 1956.

Weiner, Norbert. *Cybernetics.* New York: John Wiley & Sons, 1948.

————, *The Human Use of Human Beings.* New York: Houghton Mifflin, 1950.

Wilson, Edwin O. *Sociobiology.* Cambridge, Mass.: Harvard University Belknap Press, 1975.

Woodger, J. H. *Biological Principles*. New York: Harcourt, Brace & Co., 1929.

Zeleny, Milan (ed.). *Autopoiesis, Dissipative Structures, and Spontaneous Social Orders*. Boulder, Colo.: Westview Press, 1980.

INDEX

About the Author

Mark Davidson is the science writer for the University of Southern California News Service and a freelance feature writer whose bylines have appeared in such publications as *Science Digest, Popular Science, Family Circle, Good Housekeeping, Argosy, Architectural Digest, Los Angeles Magazine,* and the *Los Angeles Times.* He has been a member of the communications faculties at USC, UCLA, West Los Angeles College, and the California State University campuses at Northridge and Fullerton. A former prime-time talk-show host for KHJ-TV in Los Angeles, he also has produced and written more than four hundred local and nationally syndicated TV documentaries and has received a national Emmy for outstanding individual achievement in writing. He has been elected to the National Association of Science Writers, the American Society of Journalists and Authors, and the Society of Professional Journalists. Born and raised in New York City, Davidson majored in political theory and was appointed a reader in that subject at UCLA, then became a Sackett Scholar at the Columbia University Graduate School of Journalism. He began his writing career as a reporter for the Newark (N.J.) *Evening News.*

Uncommon Sense was composed in the typeface Palatino by Real-Time Typesetting, Santa Monica, California.